Microworlds

TEACHER'S GUIDE

SCIENCE AND TECHNOLOGY FOR CHILDREN

NATIONAL SCIENCE RESOURCES CENTER
Smithsonian Institution–National Academy of Sciences
Arts and Industries Building, Room 1201
Washington, DC 20560

NSRC

The National Science Resources Center is operated by the National Academy of Sciences and the Smithsonian Institution to improve the teaching of science in the nation's schools. The NSRC collects and disseminates information about exemplary teaching resources, develops and disseminates curriculum materials, and sponsors outreach activities, specifically in the areas of leadership development and technical assistance, to help school districts develop and sustain hands-on science programs.

STC Project Supporters

National Science Foundation
Smithsonian Institution
U.S. Department of Defense
U.S. Department of Education
John D. and Catherine T. MacArthur Foundation
The Dow Chemical Company Foundation
E. I. du Pont de Nemours & Company
Amoco Foundation, Inc.
Hewlett-Packard Company
Smithsonian Institution Educational Outreach Fund

This project was supported, in part, by the
National Science Foundation
Opinions expressed are those of the authors and not necessarily those of the Foundation

ISBN 0-89278-665-5

Published by Carolina Biological Supply Company, 2700 York Road, Burlington, NC 27215.
Call toll free 800-334-5551.

This material is based upon work supported by the National Science Foundation under Grant No. ESI-9252947. Any opinions, findings, and conclusions or recommendations expressed in this material are those of the author(s) and do not necessarily reflect the views of the National Science Foundation.

CB787029803

♻ Printed on recycled paper.

Foreword

Since 1988, the National Science Resources Center (NSRC) has been developing Science and Technology for Children (STC), an innovative hands-on science program for children in grades one through six. The 24 units of the STC program, four for each grade level, are designed to provide all students with stimulating experiences in the life, earth, and physical sciences and technology while simultaneously developing their critical-thinking and problem-solving skills.

Sequence of STC Units

Grade	Life, Earth, and Physical Sciences and Technology			
1	Organisms	Weather	Solids and Liquids	Comparing and Measuring
2	The Life Cycle of Butterflies	Soils	Changes	Balancing and Weighing
3	Plant Growth and Development	Rocks and Minerals	Chemical Tests	Sound
4	Animal Studies	Land and Water	Electric Circuits	Motion and Design
5	Microworlds	Ecosystems	Food Chemistry	Floating and Sinking
6	Experiments with Plants	Measuring Time	Magnets and Motors	The Technology of Paper

The STC units provide children with the opportunity to learn age-appropriate concepts and skills and to acquire scientific attitudes and habits of mind. In the primary grades, children begin their study of science by observing, measuring, and identifying properties. Then they move on through a progression of experiences that culminate in grade six with the design of controlled experiments.

Sequence of Development of Scientific Reasoning Skills

Scientific Reasoning Skills	Grades					
	1	2	3	4	5	6
Observing, Measuring, and Identifying Properties	◆	◆	◆	◆	◆	◆
Seeking Evidence Recognizing Patterns and Cycles		◆	◆	◆	◆	◆
Identifying Cause and Effect Extending the Senses				◆	◆	◆
Designing and Conducting Controlled Experiments						◆

The "Focus-Explore-Reflect-Apply" learning cycle incorporated into the STC units is based on research findings about children's learning. These findings indicate that knowledge is actively constructed by each learner and that children learn science best in a hands-on experimental environment where they can make their own discoveries. The steps of the learning cycle are as follows:

- Focus: Explore and clarify the ideas that children already have about the topic.

- Explore: Enable children to engage in hands-on explorations of the objects, organisms, and science phenomena to be investigated.

- Reflect: Encourage children to discuss their observations and to reconcile their ideas.

- Apply: Help children discuss and apply their new ideas in new situations.

The learning cycle in STC units gives students opportunities to develop increased understanding of important scientific concepts and to develop positive attitudes toward science.

The STC units provide teachers with a variety of strategies with which to assess student learning. The STC units also offer teachers opportunities to link the teaching of science with the development of skills in mathematics, language arts, and social studies. In addition, the STC units encourage the use of cooperative learning to help students develop the valuable skill of working together.

In the extensive research and development process used with all STC units, scientists and educators, including experienced elementary school teachers, act as consultants to teacher-developers, who research, trial teach, and write the units. The process begins with the developer researching the unit's content and pedagogy. Then, before writing the unit, the developer trial teaches lessons in public school classrooms in the metropolitan Washington, D.C., area. Once a unit is written, the NSRC evaluates its effectiveness with children by field-testing it nationally in ethnically diverse urban, rural, and suburban public schools. At the field-testing stage, the assessment sections in each unit are also evaluated by the Program Evaluation and Research Group of Lesley College, located in Cambridge, Mass. The final editions of the units reflect the incorporation of teacher and student field-test feedback and of comments on accuracy and soundness from the leading scientists and science educators who serve on the STC Advisory Panel.

The STC project would not have been possible without the generous support of numerous federal agencies, private foundations, and corporations. Supporters include the National Science Foundation, the Smithsonian Institution, the U.S. Department of Defense, the U.S. Department of Education, the John D. and Catherine T. MacArthur Foundation, the Dow Chemical Company Foundation, the Amoco Foundation, Inc., E. I. du Pont de Nemours & Company, the Hewlett-Packard Company, and the Smithsonian Institution Educational Outreach Fund.

Acknowledgments

The primary authors of *Microworlds* were Seliesa Pembleton and Patricia McGlashan. An early version of the unit was drafted by JoAnn DeMaria. *Microworlds* was edited by Kathleen Johnston, publications director, and illustrated by Max-Karl Winkler. Other NSRC staff who contributed to the development and production of this unit include Sally Goetz Shuler, deputy director; Joe Griffith, STC project director; and Timothy Falb, publications technology specialist. The unit was evaluated by George Hein and Sabra Price, Program Evaluation and Research Group, Lesley College.

In developing the unit, Ms. Pembleton and Ms. McGlashan worked closely with materials made available by the Smithsonian Institution Libraries, Special Collections Branch, including a first edition of Robert Hooke's *Micrographia* (1665). Invaluable guidance was provided by Lynn Margulis, Professor of Biology, University of Massachusetts, Philip Morrison, Professor of Physics, Massachusetts Institute of Technology, Phylis Morrison, Public Broadcasting Associates, and Douglas Zook, Director, Microcosmos Project, Boston University.

The NSRC would like to thank the following individuals for their contributions to the unit:

Al Banker, Teacher, Foster Elementary School, Arvada, CO

Denise Cherry, Teacher, Stuart Hobson School, Washington, DC

Ellen Farrell, Teacher, Carole Highlands School, Takoma Park, MD

Lesa Hillmer, Teacher, Carole Highlands School, Takoma Park, MD

Sally Lent, Teacher, Carole Highlands School, Takoma Park, MD

The NSRC would also like to thank the following individuals and school systems for their assistance with the national field-testing of the unit:

Becky Abraham, Teacher, Frank C. Whiteley Elementary School, Hoffman Estates, IL

Nancy Arnesen, Teacher, Frank C. Whiteley Elementary School, Hoffman Estates, IL

Bill Conrad, Math/Science Curriculum Specialist, Palatine District 15, Palatine, IL

Gary Dotterer, Teacher, Mesa Public Schools, Mesa, AZ

Waltine Eubanks, Teacher, Yancy School, Esmont, VA

Elizabeth Fordham, Teacher, John Adams Elementary School, Alexandria, VA

Don Heideger, Teacher, Frank C. Whiteley Elementary School, Hoffman Estates, IL

Pat Lloyd, Elementary Instructional Coordinator, Albemarle County Public Schools, Charlottesville, VA

Jim McDonald, Teacher, Mesa Public Schools, Mesa, AZ

Gladys Pettiford, Science Curriculum Specialist, Alexandria City Public Schools, Alexandria, VA

Bill Smith, Teacher, Mesa Public Schools, Mesa, AZ

Lily Williams, Teacher, Greer School, Charlottesville, VA

Susan Woodward, Teacher, Crozet School, Crozet, VA

Douglas Lapp
Executive Director
National Science Resources Center

STC Advisory Panel

Peter P. Afflerbach, Professor, National Reading Research Center, University of Maryland, College Park, MD

David Babcock, Director, Board of Cooperative Educational Services, Second Supervisory District, Monroe-Orleans Counties, Spencerport, NY

Judi Backman, Math/Science Coordinator, Highline Public Schools, Seattle, WA

Albert V. Baez, President, Vivamos Mejor/USA, Greenbrae, CA

Andrew R. Barron, Professor of Chemistry and Material Science, Department of Chemistry, Rice University, Houston, TX

DeAnna Banks Beane, Project Director, YouthALIVE, Association of Science-Technology Centers, Washington, DC

Audrey Champagne, Professor of Chemistry and Education, and Chair, Educational Theory and Practice, School of Education, State University of New York at Albany, Albany, NY

Sally Crissman, Faculty Member, Lower School, Shady Hill School, Cambridge, MA

Gregory Crosby, National Program Leader, U.S. Department of Agriculture Extension Service/4-H, Washington, DC

JoAnn E. DeMaria, Teacher, Hutchison Elementary School, Herndon, VA

Hubert M. Dyasi, Director, The Workshop Center, City College School of Education (The City University of New York), New York, NY

Timothy H. Goldsmith, Professor of Biology, Yale University, New Haven, CT

Patricia Jacobberger Jellison, Geologist, National Air and Space Museum, Smithsonian Institution, Washington, DC

Patricia Lauber, Author, Weston, CT

John Layman, Director, Science Teaching Center, and Professor, Departments of Education and Physics, University of Maryland, College Park, MD

Sally Love, Museum Specialist, National Museum of Natural History, Smithsonian Institution, Washington, DC

Phyllis R. Marcuccio, Associate Executive Director for Publications, National Science Teachers Association, Arlington, VA

Lynn Margulis, Distinguished University Professor, Department of Botany, University of Massachusetts, Amherst, MA

Margo A. Mastropieri, Co-Director, Mainstreaming Handicapped Students in Science Project, Purdue University, West Lafayette, IN

Richard McQueen, Teacher/Learning Manager, Alpha High School, Gresham, OR

Alan Mehler, Professor, Department of Biochemistry and Molecular Science, College of Medicine, Howard University, Washington, DC

Philip Morrison, Professor of Physics Emeritus, Massachusetts Institute of Technology, Cambridge, MA

Phylis Morrison, Educational Consultant, Cambridge, MA

Fran Nankin, Editor, *SuperScience Red,* Scholastic, New York, NY

Harold Pratt, Senior Program Officer, Development of National Science Education Standards Project, National Academy of Sciences, Washington, DC

Wayne E. Ransom, Program Director, Informal Science Education Program, National Science Foundation, Washington, DC

David Reuther, Editor-in-Chief and Senior Vice President, William Morrow Books, New York, NY

Robert Ridky, Professor, Department of Geology, University of Maryland, College Park, MD

F. James Rutherford, Chief Education Officer and Director, Project 2061, American Association for the Advancement of Science, Washington, DC

David Savage, Assistant Principal, Rolling Terrace Elementary School, Montgomery County Public Schools, Rockville, MD

Thomas E. Scruggs, Co-Director, Mainstreaming Handicapped Students in Science Project, Purdue University, West Lafayette, IN

Larry Small, Science/Health Coordinator, Schaumburg School District 54, Schaumburg, IL

Michelle Smith, Publications Director, Office of Elementary and Secondary Education, Smithsonian Institution, Washington, DC

Susan Sprague, Director of Science and Social Studies, Mesa Public Schools, Mesa, AZ

Arthur Sussman, Director, Far West Regional Consortium for Science and Mathematics, Far West Laboratory, San Francisco, CA

Emma Walton, Program Director, Presidential Awards, National Science Foundation, Washington, DC, and Past President, National Science Supervisors Association

Paul H. Williams, Director, Center for Biology Education, and Professor, Department of Plant Pathology, University of Wisconsin, Madison, WI

Contents

Goals for *Microworlds*

In this unit, students investigate both living and nonliving specimens with a variety of magnifiers, including the microscope. Their experiences introduce them to the following concepts, skills, and attitudes.

Concepts

- In order to magnify, a lens must be transparent and curved.
- Magnification is directly related to how much a lens is curved.
- Higher magnification reveals more detail in a smaller area of a specimen being observed.
- In light microscopes, lenses are combined to focus light and increase magnification.
- Scientists designed and used early microscopes to extend their observational ability and to investigate their ideas.
- Some living organisms are too small to see without magnification.
- All living things are made of at least one cell.
- When magnified, all cells have observable structures.
- Microorganisms are widespread in nature.
- Bacteria are partly responsible for the decomposition of organic material over time.
- Some bacteria are eaten by other microorganisms.
- Like all organisms, microorganisms grow and reproduce.
- Microorganisms have structures that help them survive in specific environmental conditions.
- Changing environmental conditions promote the survival of some microorganisms over others and therefore change microbial communities.

Skills

- Determining which of various objects can magnify.
- Using magnifiers, including hand lenses and microscopes, to observe living and nonliving specimens.
- Using appropriate equipment and techniques to prepare microscope slides for viewing.
- Using a microscope to observe basic cell structure.
- Communicating detailed observations through writing, drawing, and discussion.
- Making measurements of small objects using hair-widths and millimeters.
- Exploring ways to slow the movement of living microscopic specimens for closer observation.

Attitudes

- Developing an interest in exploring microscopic specimens.
- Recognizing that microorganisms have many of the same needs as other living things.
- Developing an awareness of the diversity and complexity of microbial life.
- Developing an awareness of the interactions among living things and between living things and their environment.

Unit Overview and Materials List

Microworlds is an eight-week, 16-lesson unit designed and tested for 5th grade but adaptable for use in 6th grade. The primary objectives of the unit are:

- For students to learn how to observe.

- For students to learn how to record their observations, using both writing and drawing.

- For students to learn about the properties of magnifiers.

- For students to become skilled at using hand lenses.

- For students to become skilled at using microscopes, slides, coverslips, droppers and other related apparatus.

- For students to observe a wide variety of specimens, both living and nonliving, under magnification.

The unit is composed of sequential phases that build upon one another. In the first phase, students make close observations of common objects—a penny, fabrics, screen wire, and pencil shavings. They record their observations, both by writing and drawing. These initial lessons can be used as a baseline from which the teacher can assess student progress.

In the second phase of the unit, students are introduced to different lenses—magnifying glasses, acrylic spheres, and water drops—and use them to discover that in order to magnify, an object must be transparent and curved. Students then are ready to meet the microscope, which is really just a set of lenses conveniently mounted for easy use.

In the third phase, students use the microscope to view inanimate objects. Much attention is paid to focusing and lighting techniques. Students begin by observing flat objects, such as microfiche, and newspaper and magazine photographs. They continue with hair

from their head, and use it to measure specimens. They grapple with the concept of field of view and try to decide exactly how much of an object they can see under the microscope all at once. They learn through reading about two relevant historical figures, Anton Leeuwenhoek and Robert Hooke.

Students also learn to prepare slides of different types to suit different specimens. They experiment with flat slides and coverslips, tape as a coverslip, and well slides, to decide which is most appropriate in a given situation. In addition to specimens provided in the kit, there are built-in opportunities for students to explore objects they themselves bring in. As a culmination to this phase, students observe an onion from the outside in. They predict what they think they will see, make an observation, and then record what they do see. The observation proceeds from the outer skin to a longitudinal section to a cross section, and ends with an examination of cells on student-prepared slides.

In the last phase of the unit, students must use all of the expertise they have developed in order to successfully view their new specimens: living creatures. They also must learn some new techniques for preparing slides and for slowing the motion of the microscopic creatures, while keeping in mind that these creatures are, after all, alive.

Once again, students work from the easiest specimens to view to the most difficult. They begin with *Volvox*, which is a relatively large, bright-green alga. They should have little difficulty in locating it on a slide and tracking its slow, rolling progress. Next, they observe *Blepharisma*, which is bright pink and fairly large, but faster moving. Then the vinegar eel presents real challenges. Although it is the largest living organism to be viewed, the vinegar eel is transparent, very quick moving, and not particularly pleasing to look at.

The unit closes with observations centered on the hay and grass infusions set up earlier in the unit. Since it is impossible to predict what students will find in the infusions, these lessons are best approached with a spirit of adventure. The teacher may also use them to evaluate student progress.

A few words about the appendices.

- **Appendix A** is a series of post-unit assessments.

- **Appendix B** is a checklist for recording student progress.

- **Appendix C** is a mini-art lesson for classes having particular difficulty recording observations through drawing.

- **Appendix D** provides some materials for a bulletin board or learning center.

- **Appendix E** contains notes on the care and feeding of live cultures.

- **Appendix F** is a **Bibliography** of recommended books for students and teacher.

You do not have to be an expert in microbiology to teach this unit. The background sections of the Teacher's Guide will provide you with most of the information you need. But don't be surprised if you find yourself learning along with the students, and if you and your students find yourselves faced with puzzling questions. Use this situation to model the way scientists learn; define the question, then ask, "How can we find out?" This will encourage your students to find out on their own by experimenting and consulting resource materials.

Materials List

Below is a list of materials needed for the *Microworlds* unit.

1	Teacher's Guide
15	Student Activity Books
30	hand lenses
8	pieces of screen wire (1" x 3")
8	pieces of burlap (1-inch square)
8	pieces of yarn
8	water-dropper bottles
60	pieces of waxed paper (3-inches square)
15	transparent acrylic cubes
15	transparent acrylic spheres
15	transparent acrylic cylinders
30	student microscopes, 30x
30	pieces of microfiche
30	droppers
90	flat slides
60	coverslips
60	well slides
1	package of lens paper
8	pairs of forceps
8	feathers
1	sponge, cut up
1 pkg.	fish scales
1 pkg.	poppy seeds
1 pkg.	table salt
1 pkg.	Epsom salts
1 pkg.	quartz sand
1 pkg.	grits
1 pkg.	toothpicks
1 pkg.	marbles
1	bag of hay
1	box of unflavored gelatin

1	small bottle of vinegar
*30	pennies
*30	student notebooks
* 8	small onions
* 5	cotton balls
* 2	transparencies or 2 large sheets of newsprint
* 1	large round-sided jar (quart or larger)
* 1	paring knife and cutting board
* 1	rigid ring at least 2½ inches in diameter
*	Paper towels or rags
*	Pencil shavings
*	Newspapers, black and white and color
*	Several medium-to-large glass jars with lids for making hay and grass infusions
*	Transparent tape
*	Glossy magazines
*	Hair
*	Containers for holding water to rinse slides
*	Grass
*	Scissors

Living Materials

1	live culture of *Volvox*
1	live culture of *Blepharisma*
1	live culture of vinegar eels

*Note: These items are not included in the kit. Including them would increase material and shipping costs, and they are commonly available in most schools or can be brought from home.

Teaching Strategies and Classroom Management Tips

The teaching strategies and classroom management tips in this section will help you give students the guidance they need to make the most of their hands-on experiences in this unit. These strategies and tips are based on the understanding that students already have knowledge and ideas about how the world works. And that useful learning results when they have the opportunity to think about their ideas as they engage in new experiences and encounter the ideas of others.

Classroom Discussion: Discussions effectively led by the teacher are important. The way questions are asked as well as the time allowed for responses can contribute to the quality of the discussion. When you ask questions, think about what you want to achieve in the ensuing discussion. For example, open-ended questions, for which there is clearly no one right answer, will encourage students to give creative and thoughtful answers. Other types of questions can be used to encourage students to see specific relationships and contrasts, or to summarize and draw conclusions. It is good practice to mix these questions. Always give the students "wait-time" to answer; that time (some researchers recommend a minimum of 3 seconds) will result in broader participation and more thoughtful answers.

Brainstorming: A brainstorming session is a whole-class exercise in which students contribute their ideas about a particular idea or problem. It can be stimulating and productive when used to introduce a new science topic. It is also a useful and efficient way for the teacher to find out what students know and think about a topic. As students learn the rules for brainstorming, they will become more and more adept in their participation.

To begin a session, define for students the topics about which ideas will be shared. Tell students the following rules:

- Accept all ideas without judgment.

- Don't criticize or make unnecessary comments about the contributions of others.

- Try to hitch your ideas onto the ideas of others.

Ways to Group Students: One of the best ways to teach hands-on science lessons is to arrange students in small groups of two to four. There are several advantages to this organization. It offers students a chance to learn from one another by sharing ideas, discoveries, and skills. They also will develop important interpersonal skills that will serve them well in all aspects of life. Finally, by having students work in groups, you will have more time to work with those who need the most help.

As students work, often it will be productive for them to talk about what they are doing, resulting in a steady hum of conversation. If you or others in the school are accustomed to a completely quiet room at all times, this new, busy atmosphere may require some adjustment. It will be important, of course, to establish some limits to keep the noise under control.

Planning Ahead: Being prepared is one of the keys to success with this unit. In addition to the general tips given below, watch for specific tips in lessons throughout the unit.

- Read through the Materials List in the **Unit Overview**. Begin to collect the needed items not provided in the kit.

■ Order the three living cultures. You will need **Volvox** for Lesson 12, **Blepharisma** for Lesson 13, and **vinegar eels** for Lesson 14. If you are using the *Microworlds* kit of materials from Carolina Biological, send in the prepaid order card for living materials at least 20 days before beginning Lesson 12. If not, be sure to contact your supplier of living organisms for a delivery schedule. Complete instructions for taking care of the three cultures appear in **Appendix E.**

■ Be prepared to set up the hay and grass infusions so that they will be at least two weeks old or older by the time you are ready for Lesson 15. Complete instructions for setting up the hay and grass infusions are given in Lesson 10 on pg. 63. Students should begin before Lesson 10 to collect small jars for this project. They also should begin thinking about where to collect their water specimens for the infusions. Suggestions include puddles, slow moving streams or rivers, ponds and lakes, aquariums (especially around the filter area), and bogs or swamps.

Safety: The unit contains nothing of a highly toxic nature, but common sense dictates that nothing be put in the mouth. In fact, it is good practice to tell your students that in science, materials are never tasted. Students may also need to be reminded that certain items, such as toothpicks, forceps, and water droppers, are not toys and should be used only as directed.

It is a good idea to wash hands with soap and warm water after handling onions or infusions to avoid eye irritation and ingestion of bacteria.

When using the microscope, students should never use the mirror to reflect direct sunlight through the microscope. The bright light can cause permanent eye damage.

All living cultures should be maintained in bright light but not direct sunlight. Jar lids should be loose so that oxygen can circulate. If an infusion develops mold, tighten the lid and discard it.

Handling Materials: To ensure an orderly progression through the unit, the teacher will need to establish a system for distributing and storing materials. here are a few suggestions:

■ Preview each lesson ahead of time. Familiarize yourself with the equipment and procedures. Many lessons have specific suggestions for handling the materials needed that day.

■ Organize a distribution station and train your students to pick up and return supplies to that area. A cafeteria-style approach works especially well when there are large numbers of items to distribute.

■ Organize your students so that they are involved in distributing and returning materials.

■ Consider assigning equipment and giving students the responsibility for proper care of their tools. Students should bring in shoe boxes or resealable plastic bags to house their microscopes, slides, and personal collection of specimens.

Additional management tips are provided throughout the unit. Look for the following icon.

Setting Up a Learning Center: Supplemental science materials should be given a permanent home in the classroom in a spot designated as the learning center. Such a center could be used by students in a number of ways: as an "on-your-own" project center, as an observation post, as a trade-book reading nook, or simply as a place to spend unscheduled time when assignments are done.

In order to keep interest in the center high, change it or add to it often. Here are a few suggestions of items to include:

■ Trade books on scientists who use microscopes, pictures of common objects magnified, famous discoveries in the microworld.

■ A magnifying glass, microscope, assorted slides, and interesting objects to observe, those that accompany the unit and those that do not. Objects can be brought in by students.

- Other microscopes. It would be beneficial for students to have experience with other styles of microscopes and higher-power magnification. Ask if anyone can loan your class a different microscope.

- Check the **Extensions** section in each lesson. Many of these suggestions are suitable for learning-center activities.

Curriculum Integration: There are many opportunities for curriculum integration in this unit. Look for the following icons for math, reading, writing, art, and speaking that highlight these opportunities.

Evaluation: Evaluation suggestions are included at regular intervals throughout the unit. These suggestions should help the teacher assess what students know and monitor how they are progressing. With that information it is possible for the teacher to provide assistance to students who are struggling.

Appendix A offers post-unit assessments that can be used to find out what students learned in this unit. A selection is offered so that the teacher can choose the most appropriate assessments for the students. If a pre-test is desirable, brainstorming lists from Lesson 1 could be considered. A matching post-test could then include looking at these lists and evaluating what students have learned. Among the post-assessment options is a rating scale for students to use as a self-evaluation.

Appendix B provides a black line master for a "Teacher's Record Chart of Student Progress" that you may choose to use as a checklist. It could help you in your identification of students who are not keeping up. Please keep in mind that most fifth graders will not be able to master and articulate this full list of skills.

Portfolios of student work also are useful in many ways, for example, for sharing with parents or other interested adults. A portfolio could include student notebooks with drawings, writings, and completed activity sheets. Finally, student presentations can be useful vehicles for assessment as well as useful language and critical thinking experiences in which students formulate and articulate their ideas.

LESSON 1	# Observing a Penny

Overview

In this introductory lesson, students begin to develop their observational skills by closely examining a common object—a penny. Students also discuss what they already know about magnification, lenses, and microscopes, and think about what they would like to learn.

Objectives

■ Students share their prior knowledge of magnifiers and ask more questions about them.

■ The teacher assesses students' prior knowledge of magnifiers.

■ Students set up a notebook to record their observations and ideas.

■ Students learn to use hand lenses.

■ Students discover something new in an everyday object.

Background

Observation is one of the major skills you will teach in this unit. Expect students' initial observations to be vague, overly general, and perhaps even opinionated. These early struggles will help to establish the standards for good observations. Look for observational skills to develop as the unit progresses.

Magnifiers are tools that extend the sense of sight if they are used effectively. To help students improve their observational skills and their ability to use magnifiers effectively, give them the opportunity to discover with a hand lens the two images of President Lincoln on a penny, one on each side.

There are two ways to use the hand lens. They are illustrated in Figure 1-1.

■ The first illustration shows you how to place the hand lens close to your eye, where a lens would be if you were wearing glasses. Hold the object in the other hand, and move it back and forth slowly until it is in focus.

■ Or, as the second illustration shows, hold the object stationary while keeping the hand lens above the object. Move the hand lens back and forth to focus.

Figure 1-1

Using a hand lens

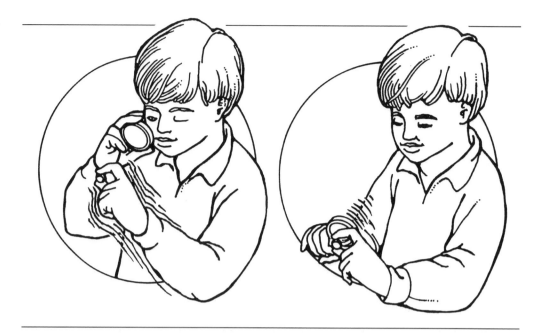

A 10-minute brainstorming session can be a very stimulating and productive introduction to magnifiers. (See **Tips for Classroom Management** on how to lead a session effectively.) The lists generated by the students also can be valuable tools for evaluation. You can use them now to determine the students' baseline of prior knowledge and again at the end of the unit to assess what they have learned.

An **Activity Sheet** has been provided for your convenience. You may prefer to have students record their observations in the notebook that they set up today. In that case, you can use the **Activity Sheet** as a model of how to set up the notebook page .

Materials

For each student

1 **Activity Sheet 1, Observing a Penny**
1 penny
1 hand lens
1 student notebook

For the class

To record student ideas and questions, have one of the following available:

2 transparencies, a marker, and an overhead projector
  OR
2 large sheets of newsprint and a marker

For optional activity:

1 small bottle of vinegar
1 small container of table salt
  Paper towels or rags

Preparation

1. Obtain the materials needed to record student ideas and questions. Label one sheet "What We Know about Magnifiers." Label the second sheet "What We Would Like To Find Out about Magnifiers."

2. Scan your collection of pennies to be sure that the statue of Lincoln is indeed visible within the Lincoln Memorial. To see Lincoln better, tip the penny back and forth slightly as you view it through the magnifier. You should see Lincoln seated between the central columns, as shown below.

Figure 1-2

Lincoln in the Lincoln Memorial

Your students will need to set up a notebook for this unit. They will use it to record their observations in writing and in sketches, and also to hold any **Activity Sheets** you choose to include. A loose-leaf notebook with pockets works well. It also is preferable to include both lined paper (for writing) and unlined paper (for drawing), if possible.

Procedure

1. Introduce the unit by telling the class that today they will begin using magnifiers to increase their ability to observe. However, before they begin, you would like them to share what they already know about magnifiers and what questions they would like to try to answer. Review the rules with the class for participating in a brainstorming session.

2. Display the sheet entitled "What We Know about Magnifiers," and record student ideas as objectively as possible.

3. Display the second sheet, "What We Would Like To Find Out about Magnifiers," and use it to record student questions.

   Keep both charts to use as you proceed through the unit.

4. For the second part of the lesson, tell students they will learn to use magnifiers and increase their ability to make detailed observations. Challenge students to find out how observant they already are by asking them to sketch both sides of a penny from memory. Distribute **Activity Sheet 1** or use this **Activity Sheet** as a model to show students how to set up the first page in their notebook.

Now give students about 2 minutes to sketch both sides of a penny from memory.

5. After students have completed their sketches, ask them to share their ideas quickly. Accept all descriptions for now.

6. Distribute the pennies and give students 1 timed minute to look at them with the unaided eye. Then have them cover up the pennies and again draw both sides in the spaces provided on the **Activity Sheet** or in their notebooks. Ask for a few quick comments on what details they were able to add to their drawings after actually observing the penny.

7. Demonstrate how to use a hand lens, and then distribute the hand lenses to the class. Challenge students to learn something new about the penny using the hand lens. Have students record their discoveries by making a drawing of the magnified penny in the spaces provided on the **Activity Sheet** or in their notebooks.

8. Collect the pennies and hand lenses.

Final Activities

Ask students to explain the following statement in light of what they experienced today: In science, we continually revise our ideas as we make new observations.

Extensions

1. Set up a penny-polishing station in the learning center. Provide vinegar, salt, and paper towels or rags. Instruct students to moisten the towel or rag with vinegar, dip it in salt, and rub the coin vigorously. Then have them observe the shiny penny with the magnifier, and compare it with a dirty one.

2. Encourage students to look at a variety of other coins as well as paper money.

3. Have students ask their parents to do the same observation exercises with the penny.

Evaluation

1. The lists generated during brainstorming can be used later as a basis for assessing what children have learned during the course of the unit.

2. Similarly, this first **Activity Sheet** or notebook entry will provide you with graphic examples of how well your students record observations at this point.

3. The notebooks students establish today will be one of your most valuable evaluation tools. They will serve as portfolios of student work containing drawings, ideas, discoveries, and questions. In most cases, they will show gradual progress in the development of observational skills.

Observing a Penny   **Activity Sheet 1**

NAME: _____

DATE: _____

1.   Draw what you remember is on a penny.

Heads   **Tails**

2.   Look at a penny for 1 minute. Then draw it again.

Heads   **Tails**

3.   Use a magnifier to observe a penny. Then draw it again. These circles are bigger because
      you will need more room for details after observing the penny with a magnifier.

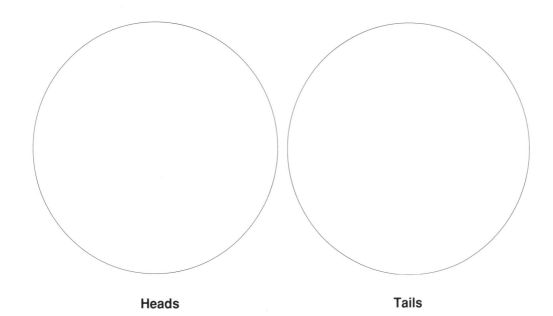

Heads   **Tails**

LESSON 2	# Communicating Your Observations

Overview

The ability to make careful observations is one of the most basic science skills. But to be of real value, observations also must be recorded and communicated. In this lesson, students continue to practice their observational skills and begin to communicate their discoveries in words and sketches.

Objectives

■ Students have more practice making detailed observations.

■ Students record their observations in both words and sketches.

■ The teacher evaluates students' observational skills.

Background

Since observation is the major focus of this unit, you will want to help your students differentiate observation from inference and opinion. Students often confuse the three. Simply stated, scientific **observations** are pieces of information that come to you directly through one of your five senses. The observed characteristics of an object are known as its **properties**. For example, your sense of touch tells you that ice cream is cold. Coldness is one of the observable properties of ice cream.

Neither inference nor opinion has a place in making observations. An **inference** is really a conclusion based on what was observed. For example, if you observe that an object is soft, cold, brown, and sweet, you may infer that the object is chocolate ice cream. But that inference may not be accurate. None of the five senses can detect the term "ice cream." A description of ice cream as disgusting or delicious is an expression of **opinion**, not of objective information collected by your senses.

These may seem like fine points, but if students are to make accurate, specific, clear observations, they need to become aware of these distinctions.

Students also need to learn to draw what they actually see, not what they think they should see. Using descriptive words to communicate is essential, but sometimes it is more effective to convey information in pictures. To help students draw what they see, you might want to consider the Supplementary Drawing Lesson in **Appendix C**. You also might want to integrate your art and science lessons for the next few sessions.

Students should be encouraged to draw like scientists. A scientific drawing is a valuable record of an observation, and, as such, it should be clear, complete, and accurate. Finally, although scientific drawings are often quite beautiful, that is a pleasant by-product, not a requirement.

Materials

For each student

1   student notebook
1   **Activity Sheet 2, Communicating Your Observations**
1   hand lens

For each team

1   set of objects:
        Screen wire
        Burlap
        Yarn
    Pencil shavings

Figure 2-1

Screen wire, burlap, and yarn viewed through a hand lens

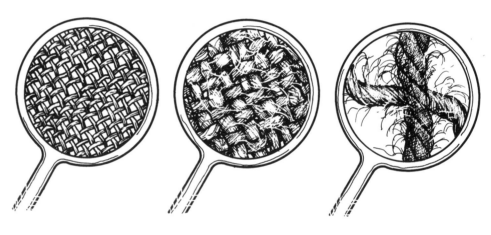

| Screen Wire | Burlap | Yarn |

Preparation

1.   Set up a distribution station for the materials. One effective way is to arrange all of the objects on a table for students to pick up "cafeteria-style."

2.   Establish the four-member student teams that you think will work well together for the duration of the unit. You may wish to further subdivide each team into two sets of partners.

3.   Decide on the object you will use in Step 2 of the **Procedure**. You could wear a large piece of jewelry, set a conspicuous article on your desk, or attach a noticeable object to the bulletin board.

4.   Empty out the pencil sharpener and place the contents on the distribution table.

Procedure

1. Begin with a brisk review of the five senses and the kinds of information each brings in. Explain that although all of the senses are important in making observations, this unit will concentrate mainly on the sense of sight.

2. Towards the end of the discussion, quickly cover up the highly visible object you selected for the observation game that follows. (See **Preparation** #3 above for suggestions.) Explain the rules of the game:

   ■ The first player gives a word, a phrase, or a sentence that describes one observable characteristic of the hidden object. (Example: smooth.) Reminder: no naming the object and no opinions of the object, please.

   ■ The second player must identify the sense that would provide the first player with that description. (Example: touch.)

   ■ The game continues until students run out of observable characteristics, and the last player is forced to name the hidden object.

3. Now that students have had some practice observing and describing what they see, distribute **Activity Sheet 2** and preview it with the class. Alternatively, use the **Activity Sheet** to show students how to set up their notebook page for this lesson.

4. Have students pick up the remainder of the materials. Allow them sufficient time to observe the objects and to record their observations in writing and in sketches.

   While the students work, you will want to circulate around the room to assess their progress, to encourage them to use more than one sense when observing, and to remind them to draw what they see.

5. Ask each group to return all materials to the designated place.

Final Activities

1. Tell students to fold their **Activity Sheet** lengthwise so that the column marked "Name of the Object" is hidden. They then exchange papers with another person on another team in the class. Each student looks at this new paper and tries to identify the objects from the classmate's description. Students quickly jot down their identifications.

2. The students who have exchanged papers should then get together for a brief discussion with each other. Suggest that they tell each other the reasons for their identifications. Ask them to compare their two papers to note the similarities and differences in their descriptions.

3. Finish with a whole-class discussion. Ask: "What qualities of the object made it easy to identify that object from its description?" "Did using more than one sense aid in the identification of an object?" Ask students to share examples of especially vivid descriptors or accurate sketches.

Extensions

1. Post a description of a "secret object" in the room. Provide a shoe box or an envelope where students can submit their answers.

2. Invite students to create a cinquain poem featuring an object of their choice. This style of poetry requires that observable properties be used to describe an object. The format for a cinquain poem and an example are below.

Noun .... person, place, thing (very general noun)

Adjective, Adjective .... two properties of the noun

Descriptive phrase .... three-word phrase describing something the noun does, is used for, or something that happens to the noun

Adjective, Adjective .... two additional properties of the noun

Synonym for the noun .... specific name of the noun

Figure 2-2

Example of cinquain poem

Fruit
Round, red
Hanging from trees
Crisp, sweet
Apples.

----Sil P.

Evaluation

These first observations can serve as a preassessment of observational skills. Although you can't expect student observations at this stage to meet all the standards listed below, it is important to establish standards.

To assess written and verbal descriptions, the following criteria may be useful:

- The student should have selected observable properties to describe.

- Another person reading or hearing the description should be able to identify the object.

To assess the sketches, try to ignore the enormous range you will undoubtedly find in drawing ability. Instead, try to decide if the following is true:

- The drawing shows that the student has in fact observed an object and has drawn what was seen.

- The drawing has an "individual character" and is not a stereotype of what the student expected to find.

- There is an attempt to show relative size, shape, texture, shading, position, and complexity.

Finally, all observations should be communicated with clarity, completeness, and accuracy.

You will need to provide the following for the next lesson:

- a large clear, round jar of water (quart or larger)
- several pages of black-and-white newsprint

Activity Sheet 2

NAME: _____

DATE: _____

Name of Object	Observable Properties	Sketch

Fold

Fold

LESSON 3

Learning about Lenses

Overview

Students have now had several experiences using the hand lenses. In this lesson they investigate the properties of lenses by testing various shapes to find out which ones act as magnifiers. By the end of the lesson, students should understand that to act as a magnifier, an object must be transparent and convex. By working with water drops, they also will discover that, the more curved an object is the more it magnifies.

Objectives

■ Students experiment with different shapes to learn which ones magnify.

■ Students discover the properties common to all objects that act as magnifiers.

Background

Light is necessary for sight. We can only see objects as they reflect light back to our eyes. If that light is bent by a transparent convex lens, the image appears magnified. The lens of a magnifying glass is usually curved on both sides, forming a double-convex shape.

Magnification does not occur when light travels through a flat surface. For example, a cube and the flat ends of a cylinder do not magnify.

Figure 3-1

A cube and the flat ends of a cylinder do not magnify

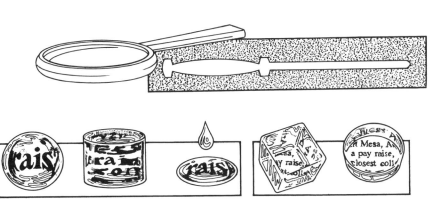

Magnification power is a comparison of the actual size of the object and the size it appears to be when viewed through a lens. For example, a 10-power lens (usually written 10x) makes an object appear about ten times larger than it actually is. Magnification power is directly related to how much a lens is curved. For example, the smaller water drop in this lesson magnifies more because it is more curved than the larger one. A 10x lens is more curved than a 3x lens.

Materials

For each student

1   hand lens
1   **Activity Sheet 3, Learning about Lenses**
1   student notebook

For each team

1   water-dropper bottle
4   pieces of waxed paper (about 3-inches square)
2   transparent acrylic cubes
2   transparent acrylic spheres
2   transparent acrylic cylinders
4   pieces of newspaper (3-inches square)

For the class

1   large, clear, round jar of water (quart or larger)

Preparation

1.   Cut the newspaper and the waxed paper into squares of about 3" x 3".

2.   Fill the water-dropper bottles and snap the spouts securely into place.

3.   Arrange the materials for each team in the distribution station for easy "cafeteria-style" pickup. You may wish to have student helpers prebag the supplies for each team to speed up distribution.

4.   Set out the large, round jar in a prominent place in the room after filling it three-quarters full with water.

Procedure

1.   Designate one person from each team to pick up all supplies for the group. Explain that the teams of four will share equipment but that students will work individually.

2.   Distribute **Activity Sheet 3** and preview it with the class. Alternatively, use the **Activity Sheet** format to show students how to set up this page in their notebooks. Students may now follow the directions for the activity on pg. 5 of the Student Activity Book. An outline of the directions is given below. Use this to preview the activity with your students.

- Select a small word on your piece of newspaper and underline it.

- Select one of the acrylic shapes to work with (you will get to work with all three).

- Examine the shape and predict whether it will magnify the word. Record your prediction.

- Now test the shape. Lay it on the word you underlined on the newspaper. Record the results. Did the shape magnify your word or not?

- Sketch what you see.

- Now do the same thing with the other shapes.

3. Once students have finished testing all the solid objects to see if they magnify, they will test with a water drop. Students can follow the directions on pg. 6 of the Student Activity Book. An outline of the directions is given below. Use this to preview the activity with your students.

- Lay a piece of waxed paper on top of the underlined word and see if the word is magnified.

- Take the waxed paper off of the word and put one drop of water on the waxed paper. Examine the water drop from the top and side. Based on what you have learned about which shapes magnify, predict whether the drop will magnify and record your prediction.

- Finally, slide the waxed paper and water drop onto the word. Does the water drop magnify? Record in words and sketches the results of the test.

Note: In previewing these activities, emphasize the sequence students should follow:

- Look at the shape and predict whether it will magnify or not, then record the prediction. Remind students that a prediction is a way of thinking into the future about results we expect. As such, it is never right or wrong but, rather, an interesting record of our thoughts. Therefore, students should not go back and correct predictions.

- Test the object and record the results.

- Sketch what is seen.

4. Allow students sufficient time to complete the activities. You may want to circulate, encouraging students to observe closely. Ask: "Have you looked through the shape from different angles?" "How does one shape compare with another?" "How much of your underlined word were you able to see through each shape?"

5. After students have completed their observations, discuss the common properties of magnifiers. Ask: "Which shapes acted as magnifiers?" "What properties do they share?" "Which shapes did not magnify?"

6. Distribute the hand lenses. Ask students how the hand lens is like the other objects that acted as magnifiers. (All are clear with curved surfaces.)

7. Have students return all materials to their designated place.

Final Activities   Show the class the large jar of water. Ask students to make a prediction based on their experiences today with shapes that magnify. Ask: "Will the jar of water act as a magnifier?" Then ask for a thumbs-up or thumbs-down. Place your hand directly behind the jar to show that it is indeed magnified. A ruler also makes a dramatic example. Ask students to explain the reasons why the jar acted as a magnifier.

Figure 3-2

*Magnifying
properties of a
jar of water*

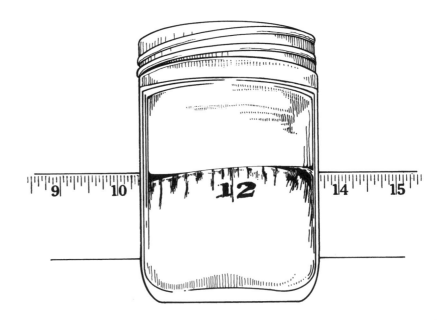

Extensions

1. If interest in the jar is high, leave it in the learning center for additional student experiments. Let them try dropping objects into the jar to watch it magnify that way, too.

2. Ask students to look for more lenses in their daily lives. Eye glasses, binoculars, telescopes, cameras, overhead projectors, movie and slide projectors, and copy machines all use lenses.

3. Using the same technique they used with the water drops, students may test small quantities of other nontoxic liquids.

Evaluation

Look for:

■ Comprehension of the properties of magnifiers

■ Ability to work methodically

■ Continued improvement in recording detailed, clear, and accurate observations

Invite students to bring in any interesting objects that they want to look at with a hand lens. These will be an important part of the next lesson.

Activity Sheet 3

NAME: _____

DATE: _____

Sketch and label the object	Predict: Will this object magnify?	Test: Does this object magnify?	Sketch the underlined word as it looked through the object

<table>
<tr><td></td><td># Looking through Lenses</td></tr>
</table>

Overview

In the last lesson, students learned the characteristics common to all magnifiers: they are transparent and convex. Today students will use lenses again to explore several common objects. Towards the end of the lesson, they should be ready for an evaluation on lenses.

Objectives

- Students have more experiences with magnifying lenses.

- Student review the properties of magnifying lenses.

- Students become more aware of the process of focusing a lens.

- Students begin to become aware of how much of an object is in the field of view.

- The teacher evaluates student progress.

Background

Before going on to the microscope in Lesson 5, students will need more experience with hand lenses. They will need to begin developing an awareness about what to do to focus the lens and what portion of an object they actually see through the lens. This will help them in future lessons when they struggle to bring the microscope into focus and when they deal with the "field of view" concept.

You may have asked students to bring in objects they are interested in looking at through lenses. Ask them to place their objects in the learning center to share with the class. Some of these objects could be used only for this lesson. You can also improvise. There is enough stuff in any normal classroom to keep the kids going for weeks.

Fun things to look at include

- In the classroom: chalk, pencil points and eraser crumbs, paper clips, paper, dust

- On you: skin, nails, hair, pocket lint, fabric, wristwatch, shoe soles

- From the playground: rocks, leaves, soil, insects, dandelions, grass

- From the cafeteria: small pieces of bread, fruit, chips, salad items

Materials

For each student

   1 **Activity Sheet 4, What Have You Learned about Lenses?**
(evaluation)

   1 marble for the evaluation

   1 hand lens

   1 student notebook

For each team

   1 set of transparent acrylic shapes from Lesson 3

   1 water-dropper bottle

   4 pieces of waxed paper (3-inches square)

   1 set of objects from Lesson 2:

        Screen wire

        Burlap

        Yarn

        Pencil shavings

      An assortment of objects brought in by students

For the class

   1 large jar of water from Lesson 3

Preparation

1.   Duplicate **Activity Sheet 4.**

2.   Refill water-dropper bottles if necessary.

3.   Place the large water jar in a prominent place to use as a focal point in the review segment of the lesson.

4.   Set out the supplies (but not the **Activity Sheet** and the marble) in the distribution station for easy pickup.

Procedure

1.   Begin the lesson with a review of the properties of a magnifying lens. To reinforce key concepts, refer to the large "magnifying jar." If students brought objects and dropped them into the jar, refer to them and how, from the side, they are magnified.

2.   Distribute the hand lenses. Ask students to look at their hand lenses and then explain to a partner what properties make them magnifiers. Ask them to share some of their explanations with the class.

3.   Have one student from each team pick up the supplies for their team.

4.   Tell students that for about 20 minutes they will be looking at a variety of different objects of their choosing, using a variety of different lenses.

Students are given guidelines for this activity in the Student Activity Book. These are outlined for you below:

- Concentrate on one object at a time. Look at it with different kinds of lenses. Do the same for other objects.

- Sketch your favorite object in your notebook. On the same page, write today's date, the name of the object, and the lens you used to look through to make the drawing.

■ Try to become more aware of how you bring an object into good focus (either by moving the object or the lens back and forth until the focus is clear).

■ Notice how much of an object you can see through a lens at one time.

5. After about 20 minutes of observations, ask students to clean up and return all supplies to the designated area.

Final Activities

Very briefly discuss a few of the interesting observations students wish to share.

Evaluation

Distribute **Activity Sheet 4** and the marble for students to use in Question No. 4 of the **Activity Sheet**.

Allow students sufficient time to complete the evaluation. The answers are given below for your convenience.

1.) B and D

2.) C

3.) Answers will vary. Students might mention cameras, eyeglasses, telescopes, binoculars, microscopes, movie or slide projectors, overhead projectors, or copiers.

4.) Answers will vary. Students should include some of these properties: round, smooth, hard, shiny, opaque (not transparent), solid.

5.) Answers will vary. The description should mention that a magnifying lens must be transparent and curved. Its function is to make things look bigger.

To build anticipation for beginning work with microscopes, you might assign the **Reading Selection** on pg. 11 of the Student Activity Book (the Background section on pg. 32 of the Teacher's Guide).

What Have You Learned about Lenses?   **Activity Sheet 4**

NAME: _____

DATE: _____

A
Window

B
Clear marble

C
Black marble

D
Goldfish bowl

E
Clear cube

1.   Look at the objects shown above. Which objects will magnify? Circle the letters of the objects that will magnify.

2.   Which of the drawings below looks most like the side view of a water drop on waxed paper? _____

A   B   C   D

3.   Name a tool or piece of equipment you may have used or seen at home or at school that has a lens.

_____

4.   Carefully observe the object your teacher has given you. List five properties of that object.

_____   _____

_____   _____

_____

5.   Describe a magnifying lens. What can it do? You may use the back of this paper.

LESSON 5

Learning to Use the Microscope

Overview

On this exciting day, students delve even deeper into the subvisible world. The microscope is not an easy tool to learn to use correctly, but the reward is well worth the effort. Today's lesson is teacher directed, and it will lay the foundation for correct use. Eventually, students will become skilled enough to work independently with the microscope.

Objectives

- Students acquire background information about the microscope.

- Students learn the functions of the parts of a microscope.

- Students learn how to adjust the light and how to focus the microscope.

- Students develop the concept of a field of view.

Background

The following information about Anton Leeuwenhoek is provided to students at the opening of Lesson 5 in the Student Activity Book. You may already have assigned this as background reading. If not, you may use this reading selection to begin this lesson.

Figure 5-1

Early explorers

Who Invented the Microscope?

Who invented the microscope?

It's hard to say. But we do know that the first person to make and use a lot of microscopes (more than 240 of them in his lifetime) was a Dutchman named Anton Leeuwenhoek.

Leeuwenhoek lived in the 1600s in the Netherlands, and he owned a store full of cloth and pincushions for sale. But the store was never open because Leeuwenhoek preferred to spend his time trying to create pieces of glass that would help him see small things.

After grinding many pieces of glass, trying to create lenses, Leeuwenhoek succeeded in making a microscope. Here's an illustration of what it looked like.

Figure 5-2

One of Leeuwenhoek's microscopes (about actual size)

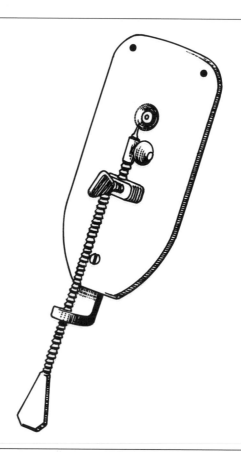

Most of Leeuwenhoek's microscopes were tiny things, not much larger than 1" x 2". And he had lenses to match—small, polished rock crystal, even a polished grain of sand.

Exciting things were happening all over the world at the time Leeuwenhoek lived. People from the Netherlands and other countries were exploring the seas and new worlds, trading their goods with other cultures. The painters who would become known as the "Dutch Masters" (including Rembrandt and Vermeer) were creating works of art that we instantly recognize today.

More fascinating to Leeuwenhoek than new lands or, possibly, even the new paintings, was what he could see with his simple microscopes, including one-celled plants and animals. He was the first person ever to see these creatures. One of the first times he ever saw bacteria was when he scraped some of the plaque from his teeth and looked at it under his lens. He looked at the blood of mammals and found that they have round blood cells, while other animals—birds, amphibians, and fishes—have oval ones. He was the first to see the *Volvox* (a creature you will have some experience with in a later lesson).

Today, only nine of Leeuwenhoek's microscopes are left. Wouldn't it be interesting to look through one? Do you think you would see different things than you see through the microscopes we have today?

Materials

For each student

1   microscope
1   piece of microfiche (with an interesting message and possibly an illustration)
2   slides
1   student notebook

Students often want to take ownership of the microscope and the objects they are observing. If possible, devise a storage system that allows this. Some teachers ask students to bring in shoe boxes or large, resealable plastic bags. Students can then keep all of their supplies close at hand to use during unassigned time, too. They also can easily add items to their collections.

Preparation

1.   Set out the materials in the distribution center for easy pickup.

2.   Become familiar with the microscope. Try adjusting the light with the mirror and focusing on the microfiche. See Steps 5, 6, 7, and 8 of the **Procedure** section for more details.

Figure 5-3

Microscope

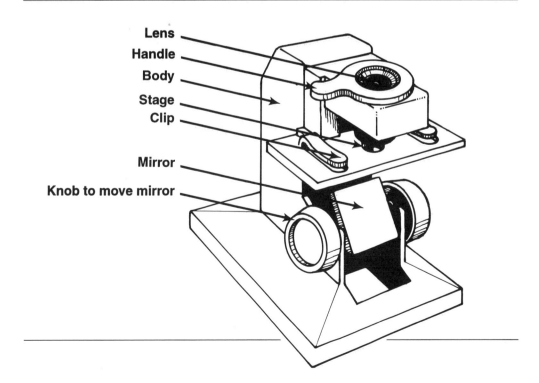

Procedure

1. Assign as background reading the **Reading Selection** entitled "Who Invented the Microscope" on pg. 11 of the Student Activity Book (the **Background** section on pg. 31 of the Teacher's Guide).

2. Hold a brief discussion to help students link their previous study of lenses with the way a microscope works. Bring out these points in the discussion:

   ■ In order to focus the hand lens, you had to move it back and forth until the image was clear. The same will be true of the microscope.

   ■ Often you were not able to see an entire object at once through the hand lens. The field of view was limited. The same will be true but to an even greater degree with the microscope.

   ■ The lenses that acted as magnifiers had a convexly curved side. This microscope has two lenses: each one is flat on one side and curved on the other side.

3. Have students pick up the microscopes, microfiche, and slides. Give them a few minutes to enjoy examining their new materials. Ask students to compare their microscope with the labeled picture on pg. 13 of the Student Activity Book (pg. 33 of the Teacher's Guide) to familiarize themselves with the names of the parts so they can follow along more easily as you demonstrate the correct use.

4. Demonstrate how to place the piece of microfiche between the two slides, and then insert this fiche sandwich under the clips on the stage of the microscope. Have students check to make sure that the microfiche is positioned over the hole in the stage. Caution students that the clips are a weak point and must be handled gently.

5. Tell students to lower the lens as far as possible by gently pressing on and turning the focus handle clockwise. Demonstrate this.

6. Have them use the mirror knob to tilt the mirror so that it captures and reflects as much light as possible up onto the specimen to be examined. Demonstrate this. Warn students **never** to reflect direct sunlight up through the lenses. This can cause permanent eye damage.

7. Now that the light is adjusted, tell students to concentrate on focusing the image. Show them how to turn the focus handle slowly counterclockwise so that the eyepiece moves up and away from the specimen. Show them how to adjust the focus by turning the handle in either direction until the image is clear.

   If students have been successful in adjusting the light and the focus, they will be able to read the message on the microfiche.

   People who wear glasses may have more success if they remove them for microscope work.

8. Ask students to tell you what they see. Draw attention to the size of the field of view by using questions such as "How many complete lines of print do you see?" and "Do you see parts of other lines?" Encourage them to move the slide around a little on the stage to view another section of the microfiche.

9. Have students return all supplies to the designated area.

Final Activities

Stress that it is important to keep size in mind as one looks at objects through microscopes. Students should keep asking themselves how much of the object they are seeing.

Ask students to start bringing in some of the printed materials they will look at in Lesson 6, especially newspapers, magazines, and comics. Other things to look at include catalogues, advertising fliers, cereal boxes, postcards, and stamps.

Extensions

1. Allow students to take apart the eyepiece of their microscope to see the two lenses. As an alternative, you might disassemble one eyepiece yourself and leave it in the learning center for students to look at.

2. Encourage interested students to read more about microtechnology. Some fascinating subjects include:

    ■ microchips

    ■ medical microbots (microscopic robots that may be able to travel inside the blood stream to clear clogged arteries, for instance)

    ■ microwaves

Figure 5-4

Microchip in the eye of a needle

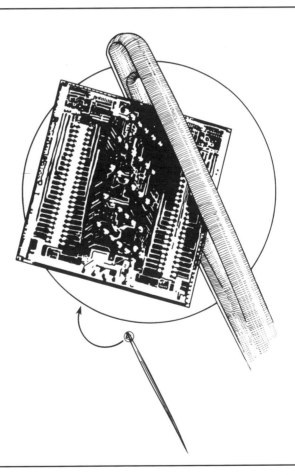

Evaluation

This lesson will give you a performance baseline from which to judge progress in students' ability to use the microscope effectively. Try to give special assistance to anyone who is having great difficulty focusing and finding the light.

<table>
<tr><td>

LESSON 6

</td><td>

Practicing with the Microscope

</td></tr>
</table>

Overview

Now that students have been introduced to the microscope, they need practice using it. The objects used in this lesson and the next are flat, dry, immobile, and easy to work with, yet are still fascinating to students. The practice they get in these lessons will help prepare them to observe the more difficult, three-dimensional, and motile specimens they meet in later lessons.

Objectives

- Students practice using the microscope with easily managed objects.

- Students continue making careful and detailed observations.

- Students continue developing their understanding of the field-of-view concept.

Background

Everyday objects seen through the microscope can take on new dimensions. Students will be excited to discover that the printed matter they look at in this lesson is actually made up of complex arrangements of dots. The black-and-white pictures in newspapers, for example, are produced by black dots on white paper. It is the size of the dots themselves that determines how light or how dark the image is. So, in the darker sections of the picture, the black dots are larger, and in the lighter sections, the black dots are smaller.

Colored pictures are made up of dots printed in combinations of the three primary colors (red, yellow, and blue), plus black. The colors are not mixed before being placed on the paper. Instead, the dots are placed so close to each other on the paper that our eyes cannot separate the colors, and we see the blend, known as an "optical mixture." So, if we look at a combination of tiny red and blue dots placed very close together, we see the optical mixture of purple.

Photographs printed on glossy magazine paper appear sharper and clearer than those in newspapers because the magazine images are printed with finer and more sharply defined dots. Since it is less absorbent, the glossy paper also prevents "bleeding" of one color into another. It may be difficult for students to see this difference at first.

If you guide students through the first segment of the lesson (Steps 1 through 6 of the **Procedure** section), they should be well equipped to work independently in the last segment. This arrangement also allows you to identify and help students who are having problems working the microscope.

Materials

For each student

    1   microscope
    1   piece of screen wire
1 or 2   strips of tape (optional)
    1   student notebook
    1   pair of scissors (optional)

An assortment of printed materials brought in by the class. These should include all four of the following types:

    Black-and-white photographs from newspapers
    Black-and-white photographs from glossy magazines
    Colored pictures from newspapers (comics are fun)
    Colored pictures from glossy magazines

Preparation

Cut up the magazines and newspapers into easily managed pieces of about a quarter of a page or so, large enough to give students a choice of viewing areas. Stack the same types of paper together for easy pickup in the distribution area.

Procedure

1. Hold a brief discussion to review the correct way to adjust light and to focus the microscope. Review Lesson 5, **Procedure** Steps 6, 7, and 8 for details.

2. Let students pick up their materials.

    Note: Students will not need to use slides today.

3. Ask students to select and cut or rip off a small strip of a black-and-white newsprint picture to observe. The strip should be about slide size and contain both light and dark areas.

    Allow students time to slip the strip under the clips and to adjust the focus. Then ask for descriptions of what they see. (Black dots on white paper.)

    Tell them to move their strip of paper around from lighter to darker sections of the picture. Ask how the sections differ. (In the lighter sections, the dots are smaller.)

4. Repeat Step 3 above using a glossy black-and-white image. Ask students to compare the newspaper picture with the glossy picture. (Both use patterns of dots to produce pictures. The dots in the glossy picture are better defined, clearer, sharper—not blurred.)

5. Next, have students select a strip of a colored picture from a newspaper showing several different colors. Suggest that they try to find a strip with what appears to be at least one clear primary color (red, yellow, or blue) and one secondary color (a mixture of two of the primary colors, such as orange or purple or green).

As students look at the strips of colored paper, ask for descriptions of what they see. Some specific questions to include are:

■ Describe the dots that make up the block of primary color. (They should all be of the same color, but a pure primary color is a little hard to find.)

■ How are those dots arranged to produce lighter or darker colors? (They are different sizes.)

■ Describe the dots that make up a block of a secondary color. (These are much more complicated, consisting of very closely spaced dots of two primary colors and possibly black.)

6. Repeat #5 above using a colored picture from a glossy magazine. Ask students to talk about how the glossy image is like the newspaper image and how it is different.

You may now decide to allow students to proceed independently and ask them to record their observations in their notebooks. Directions for these activities are repeated in the Student Activity Book on pg. 17. You may wish to preview the directions with the class before they begin.

7. Ask students to prepare a page in their notebooks to record today's observations. This kind of format works well:

Figure 6-1

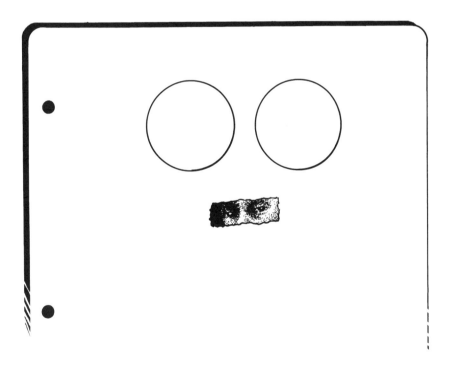

8. Next, tell students to select one of their slide-sized strips of a black-and-white newspaper picture that has a light area. Tell students to:

■ Place the screen wire over a light area on the strip of newspaper. If tape is available, they may secure the wire in place.

■ Have students slip the specimen under the clips and observe.

■ Now tell students to draw what they see in one of the squares of screen wire. How many dots are there in that one square? Tell students to count them and record the number. Stress accuracy.

Practicing with the Microscope / **39**

9. Now, tell students to repeat Step 8 above with one of their slide-sized strips of a black-and-white newspaper picture that has a dark area.

10. Ask students to write the word "micro" as small as they possibly can at the bottom of their notebook page. Then have them tear off the word and look at it under their microscopes.

Final Activities

Ask students to share with a partner their writing of the word "micro." Whose "micro" is the smallest? What kind of measurement could they do to find out?

Challenge students to think of ways to write even smaller. What kind of tools would help?

Extensions

1. In the late 1800s, a group of French artists developed a new painting technique called pointillism. They applied small dots or points of color to a surface so that they blended together when seen from a distance. Two artists who represent the pointillist style are Georges Seurat and Paul Signac.

   Ask interested students to research this style of painting. They might be able to find an example of pointillism to show to the class.

   Students might also enjoy creating their own work of art in the pointillist style.

Figure 6-2

2. Ask students to bring in postage stamps to examine under the microscope. Challenge them to determine which are printed (the image is made up of dots) and which are engraved (the image is made up of raised ink lines).

3. Expand the lesson to include observations of different kinds of papers. Focusing at the torn edge of the paper lets you see more of the individual fibers. Try newsprint, magazines, tissue, construction paper, cardboard, fine stationery, typing paper, cardboard, brown bags, and milk cartons.

Evaluation

By the end of this lesson the majority of the class should be able to:

- Correctly place an object on the stage of the microscope
- Adjust the light
- Focus easily

If any students are still having difficulty, try to give them extra help and more opportunity to practice before going on.

You will need a fairly rigid ring at least 2½ inches in diameter or larger to use in a demonstration in Lesson 7. Some things that have worked are a plastic ring from a six-pack; a circle cut from cardboard, tagboard, or a paper plate; a circular section of a paper cup.

The Field of View
(or Seeing More of Less)

Overview

In Lessons 4, 5, and 6, students were led to understand that when looking through lenses you can see only part of an object, but you see that one part in great detail. Their experiences with microfiche, screen wire, and counting dots has laid the groundwork for them to deal more specifically with the field-of-view concept. The questions now are: Exactly how much do you see when you look through the microscope? How big is your field of view? How can you measure what you see through a microscope?

Objectives

■ Students come to a fuller understanding of what is meant by field of view.

■ Students predict the size of their field of view based on past experience.

■ Students measure objects in hair-widths.

■ Students make more precise measurements in millimeters.

■ The teacher assesses students' comprehension of field of view.

Background

The **field of view** is defined as the space or area in which things can be seen through the lens of a microscope. Each time the power of a lens is increased, the field of view is decreased. So while we are seeing an object in greater detail, we also are seeing less of it. Figure 7-1 illustrates this.

Students will revisit some of the materials they observed in earlier lessons. Their familiarity with the microfiche, screen wire, yarn, pencil shavings, and newsprint may help them connect their previous experience to the idea of field of view and the relative size of objects seen in that field.

Materials

For each student

    1 microscope
    1 **Activity Sheet 5, Field of View**
    1 hair
    1 piece of microfiche
    1 flat slide

Figure 7-1

Comparing fields of view

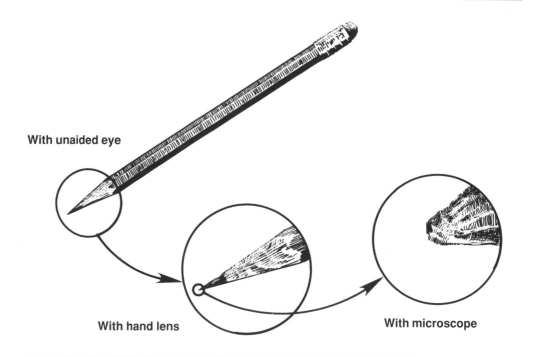

With unaided eye

With hand lens

With microscope

For each team

    1   set of objects from Lesson 2:

            Screen wire

            Burlap

            Yarn

            Pencil shavings

    1   water-dropper bottle

    4   pieces of newspaper

    1   pair of scissors

For the teacher demonstration

    1   rigid ring at least 2½ inches in diameter

    1   set of 3 to 5 classroom objects varying in size from smaller than the ring to much larger than the ring

Preparation

1. Obtain a ring to use in the demonstration of field of view. It really doesn't matter exactly what size or what it is made of as long as it is fairly rigid and the class can see it from their seats.

2. Select a set of three to five objects of various sizes.

3. Duplicate **Activity Sheet 5**.

Procedure

1. Open a discussion by remarking that one of the things students have been learning about in the last three lessons is their field of view, or how much of an object they can see through the microscope all at once. Give students an opportunity to do the mental exercise in No. 1 of **Find Out for Yourself** in the Student Activity Book. In that exercise, students are asked to imagine an object about the size of a cocker spaniel. Then, they

ask themselves, "How much ... could I see with just my eyes?," then, "About how much would I see using a hand lens," then "a microscope?"

2. Now ask students to think about the title of this lesson, "The Field of View (or Seeing More of Less)," and have them explain to a partner what that means. Have some students share their explanations with the class.

3. To reinforce the concept, give a brief demonstration of the field of view:

    ■ Hold up the ring and say that it represents the field of view of the microscope.

    ■ Then hold up an object that is smaller than the ring and ask students how much of that object they would be able to see through their field of view. (All of it.) Place the object behind the ring to test their predictions.

Figure 7-2

Demonstrating field of view with classroom objects

■ Change to an object that is larger than the ring and ask how much of that object they would be able to see through their field of view. Have them estimate some fractional part. Place the object behind the ring to test their predictions. Ask what they would have to do in order to see more of this object through their field of view. (Move the object around.)

■ Repeat the above steps using objects of varying sizes until the students have grasped the concept.

4. Have someone from each team pick up the materials.

5. Preview **Activity Sheet 5** with the class, then allow students time to complete it on their own, using the various materials supplied.

6. Clean up.

Final Activities

Closing discussion could focus on the following points:

■ the size of the circle that represents the field of view for the microscope used in this unit

■ how much fits into that field of view; how many newsprint letters, for example

■ how to measure very small objects using something like a hair

Extensions

1. Here's a challenging math extension that helps to bring home the idea that using a hair-width is an appropriate way to measure microscopic objects. The unit used for measuring microscopic objects is called the **micrometer**. The symbol for micrometer is μm. A micrometer is .001 mm, or one-thousandth (¹⁄₁,₀₀₀) of a millimeter, or one-millionth (¹⁄₁,₀₀₀,₀₀₀) of a meter. You might devise some interesting conversion exercises here if your students are interested in microscopic numbers.

    Most human hair measures about 60 micrometers across. Many microscopic organisms are considerably smaller than that. Try reproducing the picture below on the chalkboard or an overhead projector and use it to help students visualize how they might use a hair-width to measure a microscopic creature. A few questions you might ask are:

    ■   How many of these organisms would fit end to end across the width of the hair?

    ■   If these organisms fit across the width of the hair, what is the size of each?

Figure 7-3

Human hair and microbe

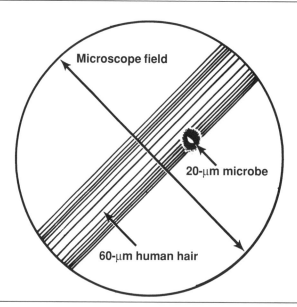

2. Ask if anyone has a compound microscope (one with different-size lenses built in) that they could bring in to share with the class. This would give students the chance to experience changes in field of view as magnifications change.

Evaluation

Activity Sheet 5 can serve as an evaluation of how well students now understand the concept of the field of view.

For your information, the answers to the **Activity Sheet** are:

1. For the JP microscope, 30x, the answer is the second from the right.

4. This depends on the microscope used. For the JP, 30x, the field of view is 4 mm.

5. Answers will vary depending on the letters viewed, but, in general, you can see three or four. Some letters, such as *i*, are smaller than others, such as *m*.

7. Answers will vary, depending on the objects viewed.

Field of View   **Activity Sheet 5**

NAME: _____

DATE: _____

1. Which of the circles below do you think represents the size of the field of view of your microscope? Put a box around the largest circle you predict you would be able to see all at once in the microscope.

    °   o   ○   ◯   ◯

2. Test your prediction. Cut out or rip off the circle at the bottom of the page that matches your prediction. Dampen the paper and put it on a slide. If you can see the whole circle at once, you may have found your field of view. If not, keep trying until you do.

3. Go back to question No. 1 and draw a diamond around the circle that you now know represents the field of view of your microscope.

4. Cut out the metric ruler below and use it to measure the circle that represents your field of view. How big is your field of view?

    _____ mm

5. Select a section of normal lettering (no big headlines or tiny stock market reports) on your piece of newspaper. Draw a circle that represents your field of view. How many letters will you be able to see at once?

    Prediction: _____ letters

    Actual number seen: _____ letters

6. One way to measure the objects you look at with the microscope is to compare them with something else whose size you already know, like a hair. Pull one hair from your head. Put about one inch of it between two slides and look at it under the microscope. Pay particular attention to how wide the hair is, not how long it is.

7. Use the width of your hair to measure as many of the objects as you can—the microfiche, the screen wire, the burlap, the yarn, and the pencil shavings. The more practice you get training your eye, the better. Ask yourself: Which is wider, my hair or the object? (It will probably be the object in most cases.)

    How many hair-widths wide is:
    Yarn? _____ hair-widths   A pencil shaving? _____ hair-widths

METRIC

    °   o   ○   ◯   ◯

LESSON 8

Preparing Slides

Overview

As the objects being viewed become more diverse, students will need to use new techniques for viewing them. In this lesson, they learn how to prepare several different kinds of slides.

Objectives

- Students learn to prepare wet-mount slides for their microscopes.
- Students learn to prepare well slides.
- Students learn to focus up and down over the surface of an object that has depth.

Background

Some objects, such as newspaper and magazine photographs, are easily viewed, and require no preparation. Some flat and dry but textured or perhaps less rigid specimens (such as fabric) are best viewed after some preparation. They work best when sandwiched between two slides that hold them in place.

Then there are small, lightweight objects (such as hair and feathers), which may require a drop of water and two slides or a slide and a coverslip to hold them in place. These are known as **wet-mount slides**. See the illustration below.

Figure 8-1

Two wet-mount slides

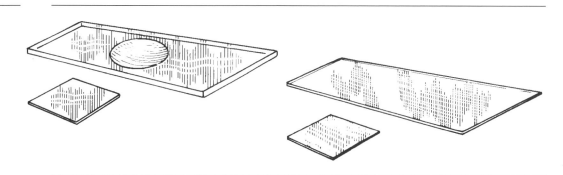

Some specimens (such as pond water or seeds) are best viewed using a **well slide**, also known as a **depression slide**. This type of slide provides a reservoir with more depth for holding thicker specimens, either wet or dry. See the illustration below.

Figure 8-2

Well slide

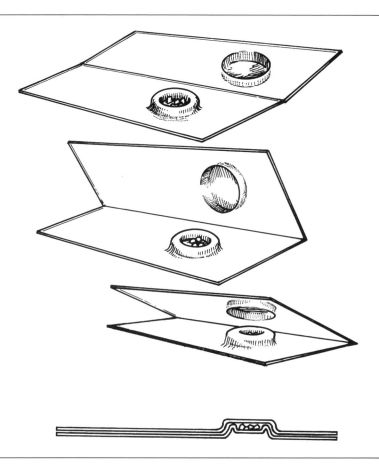

There are no strict rules about which type of slide to use in a given situation. Succeeding lessons will offer suggestions, but encourage students to experiment to find out what works best for them.

Materials

For each student
- 1 student notebook
- 1 microscope
- 2 flat slides
- 1 well slide
- 1 coverslip
- 1 hair
-   Lens paper

For each team of students
- 1 water-dropper bottle
- 1 pair of forceps
- 1 feather
- 1 piece of sponge

1 pinch of poppy seeds

8 fish scales

For the class

1 or 2 containers of clear rinse water

Newspapers or paper towels

Preparation

1. Place all supplies in the distribution center for easy pickup.

2. Set up a slide-cleaning station. You will need one or two small wide-mouthed containers to hold the rinse water, and newspapers or paper towels for the slides to drain on. Provide lens paper for polishing the slides when dry.

3. Arrange the bulletin board as suggested in the illustration below, or exhibit the pictures in some other way so that students can observe them at the end of this lesson. Black-line masters of these pictures are provided for you in **Appendix D.**

Figure 8-3

After Robert Hooke's *Micrographia*; courtesy Smithsonian Institution Libraries.

Procedure

1. Ask students how they were able to make the paper stick to the slide in the last lesson. (They wet it.) Tell them that today they will learn more about different ways of preparing slides. Because they will be viewing objects such as seeds, feathers, sponges, and, later, pond water, they will need to learn new techniques for putting these objects on a slide and keeping them there.

   Ask students to look at the pictures of the different types of slides on pgs. 23 and 24 in the Student Activity Book (pgs. 49 and 50 in the Teacher's Guide).

2. Show students the new materials they will use in this lesson, and then allow them to pick up their supplies. Remind them to handle the slides by the edges to avoid smudging them.

3. Following the directions in their books, students may do the first two activities in any order as long as everyone gets to prepare and view all of the different types of slides.

Activity 1: Preparing a wet-mount slide. (Students should use this technique for mounting the hair and the feather.)

a. Place the specimen to be viewed in the center of a clean slide.

b. Put a drop of water on top of the specimen.

c. Touch one edge of the top slide or coverslip to the drop of water, then carefully lower it over the specimen as illustrated below. To protect the microscope, blot any leaks. Then place the prepared slide on the stage.

Figure 8-4

*Preparing a
wet-mount slide*

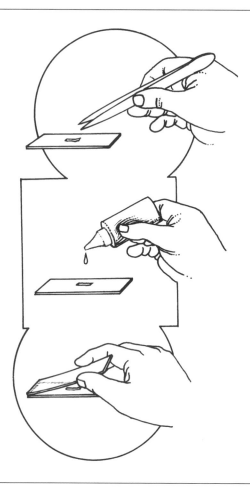

d. Alert students that air bubbles can get trapped around the specimen when they are making a wet-mount slide. They may even mistake the bubbles for the specimen itself at first, but with a little practice they will learn to recognize them. Bubbles on a slide look like this:

Figure 8-5

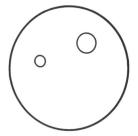

e. Remind students to make a sketch in their notebook of either the hair or the feather. Remind them to date and label the sketch.

Activity 2: Preparing a well slide. (Students should use this technique for mounting the seeds and the piece of sponge.)

a. Place the specimen to be viewed in the well. Remind students that less is better. A single layer of seeds or a thin slice of sponge is easier to see.

b. Depending on the style of the slide, either snap the lid shut (on the hinged style) or place a coverslip over the well. Then place the slide on the microscope stage.

c. Because the specimens in the well slides have depth, only part of the specimen will be in focus at any one time. It is a challenge to learn to focus up and down over the entire surface of the object to get a complete picture of it. Remind students of how to focus from the bottom up.

d. Ask students to make a sketch in their notebooks either of a poppy seed or the piece of sponge. Remind them to date and label their sketch.

Activity 3: Experimenting with mounting techniques. Using the fish scales, students should experiment with both dry and wet methods to find out which works best for this object.

4. Clean up. Direct students to the slide-cleaning station as they finish their work. A gentle swish through the rinse water is usually sufficient. Have students lay the slides out on newspaper or paper towels to air dry. They can polish them later with lens paper.

Final Activities

1. Focus class attention on the bulletin board. Ask students which of the objects pictured there they can identify through their experiences with the microscope. Really sharp observers should be able to identify No. 1 as poppy seeds, No. 2 as a sponge, No. 6 as cloth (silk), No. 7 as the period at the end of a sentence, No. 10 as a feather, and No. 11 as fish scales.

    Now that you have piqued their interest, encourage students to find out what the other objects are. For your information, they are No. 3, a fly and its wing; No. 4, a fly's head; No. 5, cork; No. 8, a bee's stinger; and No. 9, crystals in flintstone.

Extensions

Seeds are an interesting subject for the microscope. Encourage students to check the spice racks at home for some of the seeds shown in Figure 8-6 and to bring them in, with parental permission, of course.

Ask students to begin bringing in specimens to look at in Lesson 10. With a few commonsense precautions, almost anything they are interested in looking at will work. More details will follow in Lesson 9.

Figure 8-6

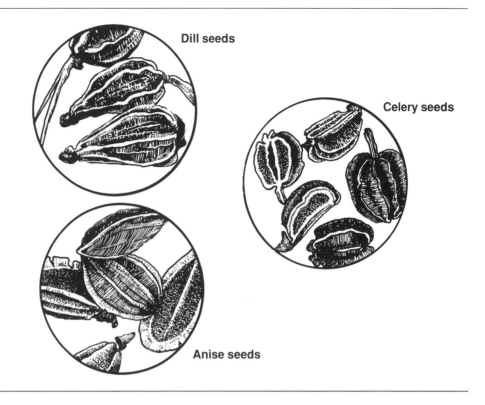

Dill seeds

Celery seeds

Anise seeds

What Is It?

Overview

This lesson challenges students to apply their new skill at making well slides and at focusing on surfaces of three-dimensional objects. They will attempt to identify unknown specimens, working with two common crystals and two noncrystals.

Objectives

■ Students identify unknown specimens through observation.

■ Students apply their skills viewing three-dimensional objects under the microscope.

■ Students learn to prepare their own well slides properly.

Background

The unknown specimens for this lesson were selected because to the naked eye they look very similar. Under the microscope, however, it is easy to see that two of them, salt and Epsom salts, have distinctive crystal shapes. The other two, sand and grits, have irregular shapes. Below are brief descriptions of each of these specimens. Students will find this information on pgs. 30 and 31 of the Student Activity Book and will use it to identify these specimens. Be careful not to give the answers away!

1. Table salt

Figure 9-1A

Table salt

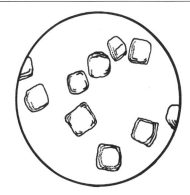

Table salt, or sodium chloride, is easy to recognize because of its translucent, cube-shaped crystals. One of the most common minerals, it is found in great abundance both in the earth and in seawater.

2. Epsom salts

Figure 9-1B

Epsom salts

Epsom salts, a magnesium sulfate compound, has distinctive needle-shaped crystals that range from transparent to white. This salt is named for Epsom, England, where it was prepared from the water of local mineral springs. It is a medication used both internally as a laxative and externally to reduce inflammation.

3. Quartz sand

Figure 9-1C

Quartz sand

Characteristically, quartz has a regular six-sided crystal. Quartz sand, however, shows the result of weathering. Wind, water, and temperature all contribute to breaking up quartz crystals into the smaller irregular shapes of quartz sand.

4. Grits

Figure 9-1D

Grits

This is a food product made from ground corn. It is irregular in shape, and ranges from opaque to translucent. Color ranges from white to pale yellow.

Materials

For each student

1   student notebook
1   microscope
1   well slide
1   coverslip

For each team of students

1   pinch each of the following materials:

Table salt
Epsom salts
Quartz sand
Grits

Transparent tape
Lens paper

Preparation

1.   Place materials in the distribution center for easy pickup.

One efficient way to deal with distributing the four granular specimens is to pour each one into a wide-mouthed container. To prevent contamination, provide a separate spoon or paper scoop (just a strip of paper creased down the center) for each container.

Figure 9-2

Paper scoops

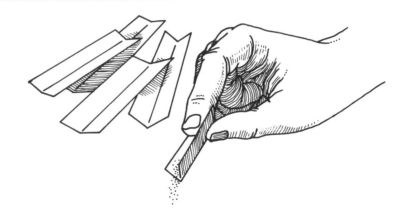

2.   Label each of the four containers of unknown specimens No. 1, No. 2, No. 3, and No. 4. Be sure that the order of the numbers does **not** match the order of the list of the specimens in the narrative in the Student Activity Book (which is in the same order as in your Teacher's Guide). Do jot down which specimens are which.

3.   Arrange students in working teams of four members each.

Procedure

1.   Briefly review with the class the techniques they used to prepare a well slide (place a very small quantity of the specimen in the well, preferably only a single layer, and cover it). Also review how they brought the three-dimensional objects, such as poppy seeds, into focus (focus on one level at a time, and slowly move focus up and down over the surface of the specimen). Tell students that they will be using these techniques today to observe and identify some mystery specimens.

2. Each team should label their well slides from 1 to 4. A small piece of tape placed close to the end of the slide works well as labels.

3. Now ask students to pick up their unknown specimens. Each member of the team should have one slide and be responsible for picking up only the specimen that corresponds to the label on his or her slide. (The student holding slide No. 1 should pick up specimen No. 1, and so on.)

4. When they return to their seats, each student should prepare a slide of the specimen he or she picked up, and then examine the slide, double-checking to make sure that there is only a single layer of granules and that individual granules are clearly visible.

5. Then, using the information about table salt, Epsom salts, quartz sand, and grits given on pgs. 30 and 31 in the Student Activity Book, each student should attempt to identify the specimen on his or her slide. They then should exchange slides with another member of their team. Using this procedure, each student will identify all four unknown specimens. Remind them to record their answers.

6. After everyone is finished, post the answers so that students may check their work.

7. If time permits, allow students to prepare mystery slides with which to challenge their teammates. The mystery slides should be a mixture of two or more of the specimens just identified. Caution students that the slides need to be carefully made if they are to be a good test of observational skills. In a mixture, it is very important to be able to see individual granules.

Final Activities

1. In a brief discussion, ask students to verbalize the key properties that helped them distinguish one specimen from another.

2. Remind students that the next lesson will center around the objects that they bring in to observe. With a few commonsense precautions, almost anything they are interested in looking at will do.

   Survey the class to find out what kinds of objects they have already collected. The discussion will probably generate ideas of additional, interesting objects to bring in. Here are a few fun things to suggest, if your students haven't already thought of them:

   ■ fruits, such as apples, bananas, pears, and peaches

   ■ vegetables, such as potatoes, carrots, lettuce, and celery

   ■ meats, such as chicken or beef

   ■ meat bones

   ■ granular materials, such as instant coffee, ground coffee, sugar, pepper, alum, soap flakes, and fruit-drink mixes

   ■ seeds, leaves, flowers, roots, and the stems of just about any plant

   Specimens that are too thick to fit under the microscope may be sliced into thin sections by the teacher or another adult. A razor works well. Or, the specimen may be lightly mashed. Then a very small portion can be used in a wet-mount slide.

Extensions

1. Salt crystals are easy to grow. Stir 3 tablespoons of salt into a cup of warm water. Pour the solution into a shallow pan (or put two or three droplets onto a slide) and set it on a windowsill or another warm place. As the water evaporates, salt crystals will form.

2. Ask students to be alert for other crystals in their environment and to share their observations with the class. They may notice such things as snowflakes, frost, rocks, or jewelry.

3. Challenge students to measure some of the specimens in this lesson in hair-widths.

4. To help students relate this activity to the world outside the classroom, invite a microbiologist or a lab technician from your local hospital to talk to the class about how they identify "mystery slides" every day as part of their job. These scientists have to be able to look at a slide and figure out what disease a patient has so that the doctor can treat it properly.

Evaluation

This lesson serves as a checkpoint in assessing students' ability to:

■ prepare slides

■ focus over the surface of a three-dimensional object

■ make close observations

Students who are still having difficulty with these skills should be given the opportunity to practice before going on to the more free-wheeling situation in Lesson 10.

Exploring Common Objects

Overview

Today's lesson is driven by whatever curious assortment of objects the students have brought in. It is a lesson best approached in a spirit of adventure, where the children's own questions and discoveries lead the way.

This also is an opportunity for students to experiment independently with different slide-making techniques and to practice making light adjustments and focusing.

Also, in preparation for Lesson 15, the class will set up hay and grass infusions to begin growing microscopic creatures.

Objectives

- Students make their own discoveries as they observe specimens they are interested in.

- Students practice preparing slides of different types.

- Students perfect their light adjustment and focusing techniques.

Background

It is impossible to predict what your students will bring in to observe under the microscope today, so be prepared to deal with a wide variety of objects. Expect, too, that there will be a high level of excitement about their discoveries as they show you and one another what they have found.

Your role is one of facilitator and orchestrator, and you will be busy. Initially, students may need help preparing specimens, making thin slices of large objects, or deciding what type of slide to use. Then, as they begin to make observations and share them with you, you will want to ask questions that encourage children to dig deeper or to look more closely. Suggest that they make sketches of their specimens, especially any that are particularly interesting or puzzling. And, finally, you may want to encourage them to read the **Reading Selection** on Robert Hooke (pg. 35 in the Student Activity Book; pg. 65 in the Teacher's Guide) and to do research in the library.

The conclusion of the lesson, setting up the hay and grass infusions in preparation for Lessons 15 and 16, is a separate activity and can be done today or later, whenever is most convenient for you. Be sure to plan this activity at least two to four weeks before Lesson 15 begins, however.

Last, be sure that you have ordered the live organisms for Lessons 12, 13 and 14. If you are using the *Microworlds* kit of materials from Carolina Biological, send in the prepaid order card for living materials at least 10 days before beginning Lesson 12. If not, now is the time to contact your supplier for a delivery schedule.

Materials

For each student

    1 student notebook

    1 microscope

    1 well slide

    2 flat slides

    2 coverslips

For each team

    1 water-dropper bottle

    1 pair of forceps

    1 hand lens

    4 pieces of lens paper

       Tape

For the class

       An assortment of objects

    1 container of clear rinse water

       Newspapers or paper towels

For setting up the hay and grass infusions

       Several medium-to-large glass jars with lids

    1 bag of hay

       Grass

       Water

Preparation

1. Set out the materials in the distribution center for easy pickup.

2. Set up the slide-cleaning station.

3. Read the information on hay and grass infusions on pg. 63. Gather together the hay, grass, and water needed for making the infusions. You could enlist student's help in getting the hay and the grass. You also should try different water sources, if possible. Students could help you by bringing in water from puddles, ponds, bogs, and so on.

4. Label the infusion jars. Include the date they are being prepared and make sure the labels also show what was placed in them.

Procedure

1. Hold a very brief, introductory discussion to set the tone of inquiry for today's activities. If necessary, you might also review techniques for making slides, focusing, and adjusting the light.

2. Now let the exploring begin. As much as possible, let students proceed at their own pace, make their own discoveries, and share their findings with teammates.

3. Circulate around the room, assisting where necessary and assessing informally. This is a good time to encourage students to look again, to look more closely, and to verbalize what they see. Encourage note taking and sketching, too, so that they will have the details of their observations should they want to do further library research on their findings.

Final Activities

1. After allowing children ample time to complete their investigations, ask for volunteers to share some of their most interesting discoveries with the class. Students might draw on the chalkboard what they saw. These students could then leave their specimens in the learning center for the rest of the class to observe at a convenient time.

2. Now have the students help you set up the hay and grass infusions. Follow the directions given below.

   Making hay and grass infusions is one of the easiest and most common methods of cultivating living microorganisms. These infusions will provide the class with a source of microscopic creatures to observe in Lesson 15. You will need ordinary dried hay, any other dried grass, or some fresh grass. You can try all three, in separate containers.

   The reason that hay or dried grass will work is that many microorganisms are specially adapted to live through periods of little or no water. They survive drought in an encapsulated state and can resume an active life when introduced to an environment that provides food and water. First, bacteria will begin to grow, using the hay or the grass as a food source, then larger creatures, which feed on the bacteria. See Lesson 15 for further details.

   The important thing to remember is that the kind of water you use can make a difference. Water sources to consider include puddles, aquarium filters, ponds, slow-moving streams, swamps, or bogs because they are likely to contain their own microscopic creatures. Using these sources of water "stack the deck" in favor of your class being able to have creatures to observe by Lesson 15.

   1. Fill several jars one-third full of the plant matter of your choice (hay, dried grass, fresh grass).

   2. Add water to the top of the jar. River, stream, pond, swamp, bog, or aquarium water works best, but if these are not available you can use distilled water or tap water left standing for 24 hours to allow the chlorine to evaporate.

   3. Cover the jars loosely (they need oxygen) and place them in a well-lighted place but not in direct sun. Let them stand for two to four weeks. Check them periodically to observe changes.

Exploring Common Objects / **63**

Figure 10-1

A hay infusion

**Fill jar one-third full
with hay or grass**　　　　**Fill jar with water**　　　　**Cover loosely and place
in well lighted place**

Extensions

1. Follow up on the interest generated in materials brought in by the students. Possibilities include:

   ■ Measure the specimens in hair-widths or millimeters.

   ■ Do library research on the specimen and present the findings to the class.

   Also, consider hanging some of the student drawings of specimens on the bulletin board. These make an interesting display and can be used for a kind of "Guess What I Am" game for visitors to the class.

2. Students also could read about and report on scientists who have made significant discoveries using the microscope: Louis Pasteur, Robert Koch, Alexander Fleming, Edward Jenner.

3. If they haven't already, students could read the **Reading Selection** on Robert Hooke on pg. 35 of the Student Activity Book and pg. 65 of the Teacher's Guide.

4. Write a creative story about a micronaut who journeys far into the mysterious interior of one of the specimens.

Evaluation

The students' independent work today gives you an opportunity to assess their progress in:

   ■ selecting the appropriate slide for the object

   ■ preparing a clear slide

   ■ making close observations

   ■ verbalizing what they observe

   ■ recording accurately what they observed

**Reading
Selection**

Taking a Look with Robert Hooke

Before he became a scientist, Robert Hooke wanted to be a painter. He drew some very accurate, detailed drawings of the objects he observed under his microscope over 300 years ago.

Robert Hooke and Anton Leeuwenhoek lived at about the same time, in the middle of the 1600s. While Leeuwenhoek was busy building microscopes and looking at a great variety of microbes in his little shop in The Netherlands, Hooke was busy doing somewhat the same thing in England.

One of the differences between Leeuwenhoek and Hooke is that Hooke drew what he saw through his microscopes. When he was young, Hooke thought he wanted to paint portraits. But then he went off to school and college, and he became more interested in science. Hooke liked conducting experiments to find out more about the world around us.

While he was experimenting, Hooke learned a lot about what we call physics. And he invented some tools, such as the barometer, that help us determine what is happening in the physical world. (A barometer detects changes in pressure in the atmosphere, and these changes often indicate whether a storm is coming.) He also was interested in improving microscopes. His original microscope didn't have a lot of magnifying power. Hooke saw that the reason was because the lenses weren't curved enough, so he made his own microscope with a more rounded lens.

But with microscopes Hooke really was more interested in what they could help him see. Using both simple (one lens) and compound (more than one lens) microscopes, he observed and carefully drew pictures of insects and their parts, the point of a needle, the edge of a razor, what he called insects in rainwater (they probably were microbes), snow crystals, and pieces of cork.

All of Hooke's drawings of what he saw under his microscopes are in a book entitled *Micrographia, or Some Physiological Descriptions of Minute Bodies Made by Magnifying Glasses with Observations and Inquiries Thereupon.* It was published in 1665. A copy of it can be found in the Special Collections Branch of the Smithsonian Institution Libraries. If you want to see a copy of this incredible picture book, you probably can! Just ask your librarian about helping you find the paperback edition.

Figure 10-2

*One of Hooke's microscopes
(actual size was about
9 inches tall)*

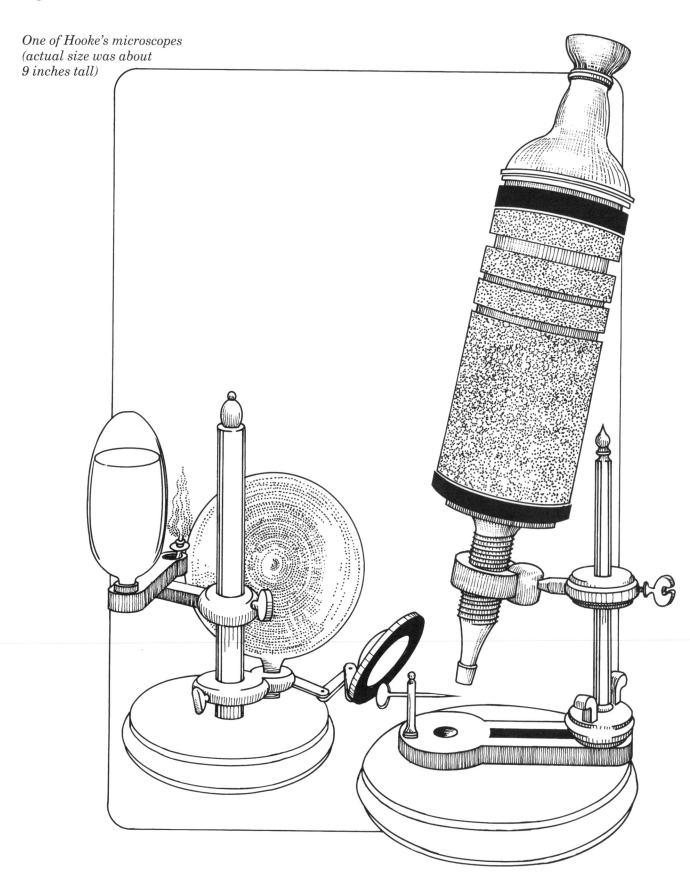

Looking Inside an Onion

Overview

When Robert Hooke looked at a sliver of cork under his microscope, he saw rows of "little empty boxes" that reminded him of rows of prison or monastery cells. He was the first to describe these structures, and in naming them, he coined a new use for the word "cell."

In this lesson, students will move from the outside of the onion in, until they reach the smallest living unit, the **cell**.

Objectives

■ Students examine and describe the internal structure of an onion.

■ Students observe and describe the cells in an onion.

■ The teacher uses **Activity Sheet 6** to evaluate student progress.

Background

It is traditional to use onions for students' first observations of a cell because it is possible to remove a thin skin from an onion that is actually a single layer of relatively large cells (about 1 hair-width wide by 3 to 5 hair-widths long).

The cellular structures that students will observe are:

■ The cell wall, which supports and gives shape to the cell. The thickness of a cell wall varies according to the type of plant cell.

■ Possibly the thin cell membrane, which lies just inside the wall (but which may or may not be visible). The membrane holds in the living parts of the cell.

■ The nucleus, or the control center for the cell, which should be visible in most intact cells. If the cell was broken open when the skin was pulled away from the onion, the contents probably were spilled out and left behind.

Figure 11-1

Onion cells

Materials

For each student

1 **Activity Sheet 6, What's Inside an Onion?**
1 microscope
1 hand lens
1 slide
1 coverslip

For each team

1 small onion
1 water-dropper bottle
1 pair of scissors
1 pair of forceps
4 toothpicks
   Paper towel or newspaper

For the teacher

1 paring knife
1 cutting board or piece of thick cardboard

For the class

1 container of clear rinse water

Preparation

1. Reproduce **Activity Sheet 6**.

2. If possible, prepare an onion slide and look at it yourself so that you will be able to give the class pointers on preparation and on making lighting adjustments.

3. Set out all materials in the distribution center for easy pickup.

4. Set up the slide-cleaning station.

Procedure

1. As a warm-up exercise, ask students to observe the outside of the onion and to describe its exterior.

2. Distribute and preview **Activity Sheet 6**. Stress that students will be making two different sketches at each different level of observation. The first sketch will record what they think they will find. The second will

record what they actually observe. Take a few moments to discuss why students should not go back and correct their initial drawings of what they think they will find. These drawings cannot be incorrect. They are predictions, and, as such, they are a record of the students' thinking, not their observations.

3. Allow students sufficient time to complete Nos. 1, 2, 3, 4, and 5 of the **Activity Sheet**. While they are working, you will need to move from group to group with the knife and cutting board.

    Note: If you blot the cut ends of the onion on paper towels, you may reduce the potential for eye irritation.

4. For No. 6 on the **Activity Sheet**, students will need to prepare a wet-mount slide of the onion skin to look at under the microscope. Each student should have the equivalent of half an onion ring. They can peel the skin from between the layers of the ring by grasping the cut edge with forceps or fingernails and gently pulling a strip free. They will need a piece about ½ inch long. Any excess can be cut off with scissors. You may wish to demonstrate the process or allow students to work independently by following the instructions on pg. 38 in the Student Activity Book.

Figure 11-2

Removing onion skin with forceps

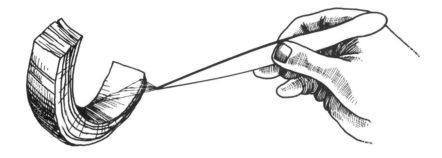

Step-by-step, the process is:

■ Separate the layers of the onions. Use your forceps or fingernails to peel off a piece of the thin skin found between the layers.

■ Hold the onion skin with your forceps. Use scissors to snip off a piece about ½ inch long.

■ Lay this piece of onion skin flat on your slide. Be careful not to fold or wrinkle it. Use a toothpick to smooth it out.

Note: If the skin does get folded, students will not be looking at a single layer of cells.

■ Squeeze a drop or two of water on top of the onion skin, then lower a coverslip or slide on top.

5. As students look at the onion under the microscope, suggest that they experiment with the lighting conditions. Moving the mirror back and forth while looking through the lens or using a hand to block the light will reveal different aspects of the cell structure. Students can create a bright field of view where the onion cell details appear dark, or they can create a dark field of view where the onion details appear white.

6. At the end of the lesson ask students to clean their slides thoroughly.

Safety Reminder

When handling onions, warn students not to put their hands near their eyes. They should wash the onion juice from their hands as soon as possible.

Final Activities

1. Cells were named by Robert Hooke because their shape reminded him of small, boxlike, prison or monastery cells. Other scientists have called cells "the building blocks of all living things." Ask children to reflect on why cells are compared to building blocks. (Students may mention that the shape and arrangement of onion cells reminds them of a brick wall. Or they may comment on the fact that living things are made up of cells.)

2. Assign background reading on the **Volvox** (pg. 41 of the Student Activity Book; pg. 73 of the Teacher's Guide).

Extensions

1. If someone has brought in a microscope with higher magnification, allow interested students to get an even closer look at a cell.

2. Encourage students interested in cellular structure to do further research on the subject. This will be an intellectually challenging task for most children this age.

3. Suggest other plant cells for students to observe:

   - Using the same technique as for the onion cells, students can observe garlic cells.

   - By slowly tearing a lettuce leaf, one can expose a single layer of cells. Examine the torn edge for a flap of transparent skin. Use it to make a wet-mount slide.

Figure 11-3

Elodea

■ The aquarium plant, *Elodea*, has leaves with a double layer of cells. Observing this plant will be more difficult, but by making frequent focus adjustments, students may be able to see these cells.

Evaluation

This lesson offers opportunities to evaluate student techniques as well as observational skills. Look for the following:

■ Students should now be able to prepare a wet-mount slide with little or no assistance.

■ Students should be able to focus with no difficulty.

■ Drawings under the "I see" heading should reflect the actual interior of the specimen. The drawings should be complete, accurate, and clear enough for you to recognize the basic structures.

What's Inside an Onion? **Activity Sheet 6**

NAME: _____

DATE: _____

Predict **Observe**

1. Sketch what you *think* you would see if you cut an onion lengthwise from the leaf end to the root end.

2. Sketch what you *see* when the onion is sliced lengthwise.

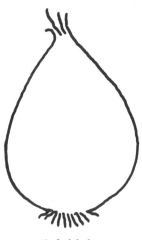 

1. I think 2. I see

3. Next sketch what you *think* you would see if you cut one of your onion slices in half across the roundest part.

4. Now sketch what you *see* when the onion is cut through the roundest part.

3. I think 4. I see

5. What do you *think* the onion will look like under the microscope?

6. Now sketch what you *see* under the microscope.

5. I think 6. I see

Looking at Living Things: *Volvox*

Overview

By now students have probably become quite adept at using their microscopes effectively. Looking at living creatures will provide them with the opportunity to put all of their microscope skills to good use, and it also will present new challenges: these creatures will move, display individual characteristics, and won't cooperate!

Each of the next three lessons will feature a different living organism, in ascending order of difficulty to view. Background information on the organism will be given at the beginning of each lesson.

Objectives

■ Students learn the best way to handle living, moving, creatures and how to prepare slides for them.

■ Students use the microscope to observe these creatures.

Background

Commonly found in ponds, **Volvox** is a member of a large group of organisms known as **green algae.** Algae do not have roots, stems, or leaves, but, like green plants, they use light to make their own food by a process known as photosynthesis. Most algae live in the water, but you also may find them on damp surfaces, such as tree trunks, rocks, and soil.

Volvox cells are especially interesting because they live together in colonies of 1,000 to 3,000 similar cells, arranged in a hollow sphere. Each individual cell has two **flagella**, or whiplike tails, which work together to propel the colony through the water. The spherical colony of cells is held together by a clear jellylike substance.

Figure 12-1

Volvox *colony*

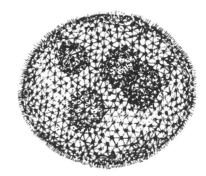

Also visible inside the sphere of many of the large colonies are smaller daughter colonies. After the daughter colonies become big enough, they will be released through an opening in the parent colony to become new, independent colonies.

There are advantages to colonial living. For example, because the *Volvox* colony is relatively large (350 to 600 micrometers), the tiny individual *Volvox* cells living in the colony are safe from the many microscopic organisms that feed on other single-celled creatures.

Volvox is one of the beauties of the microscopic world. It is a rich bright green, and the whole globe rotates slowly through the water, reminding one of an ethereal planet in graceful orbit.

Materials

For each student

1   student notebook
1   microscope
1   very clean well slide
1   piece of lens paper
1   coverslip

For the class

Volvox culture and clean droppers
1   container of clear rinse water for cleaning slides

Preparation

Set up a distribution station where students will pick up their specimen of *Volvox*.

Allowing individual students to pick up their own live specimens is bound to slow the process, especially if it is done carefully, but students will learn from it. You do need to be prepared in advance, however. You may want to plan to provide the class with a concurrent activity so that they don't waste time waiting for their turn at the distribution station.

Procedure

1. Allow time for students to read the background information on *Volvox* on pg. 41 of the Student Activity Book. It is the same as the **Background** on pg. 73 of the Teacher's Guide.

2. Hold a brief class discussion on the characteristics of *Volvox*. Ask:

    ■   What do you expect to see under the microscope today? How will *Volvox* look? How many colonies might you see? Do you think you will be able to tell one colony from another? Do you think it will be possible to see the individual cells that make up the colony?

    ■   How will looking at living things be different? What new challenges will you face?

3. Remind students that living creatures require special handling, then model how to pick up a specimen of *Volvox* from the distribution center as follows:

   ■ Using a clean dropper provided at the station, carefully draw up a very small amount of water from the jar. Try not to agitate the jar or to stir up the water.

   ■ Place one drop of the water into the clean well slide, and put on the coverslip to prevent evaporation.

   ■ Gently return any water left in the dropper to the supply jar. Drop it in from close to the surface of the water, not from high up. It may contain many other live *Volvox*, you don't want to damage them.

4. Allow students time to observe their specimens. You may want to circulate around the room, encouraging and assisting. These are relatively large and slow-moving creatures, but students may experience some difficulty in locating specimens. Then they may experience some frustration in following the creatures with their microscopes. Remind students to keep scanning back and forth on the slide and focusing slowly up and down until they find *Volvox*. They might try different lighting effects, too.

5. Remind students to include at least one drawing of *Volvox* in their notebook today and to try to label the parts. They also should write a few sentences describing what they observed, including observations of color and movement.

6. Clean up. Return specimens to the original container using the dropper. Rinse off the slides in clean water.

Final Activities

Hold a brief discussion. Ask students to report on what they observed. Here are a few items to include to get them to focus on details:

■ How many different individual colonies did you find on your slide? How could you tell them apart? (Relative size, number of daughter colonies, brightness of color.)

■ Were individual cells of the colony visible? (Not at 30x.)

■ How would you describe the motion of the colony? (Rolling, gliding, spinning.)

Extensions

1. Suggest that interested students research the subject of other **flagellates**. A **flagellate** is any creature having one or more **flagella**, or long, whiplike tail, which it uses for locomotion. A good example is the ***Euglena***.

Figure 12-2

Euglena *under the microscope*

Euglena *and its flagellum*

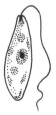

2. Students may be interested in researching the economic value of algae. Topics to investigate include:

   ■ algae as food

   ■ algae as killers, as in a red tide

3. Ask students to be on the alert for other algae to look at under the microscope. They might find other algae in ponds, aquariums, or on the top of the soil of potted plants.

4. Ask students to think about other creatures that live in colonies. You may even want to conduct a brainstorming session on this. One question to discuss is: "Of what advantage is it to these creatures to live together?"

5. Suggest that students plan a controlled experiment to find out what happens to algae deprived of light. If possible, allow them to set up and conduct the experiment to find the answer on their own.

Evaluation

Volvox is one of the largest and slowest moving of the living creatures that the class will observe. If students are having difficulty finding, focusing, and tracking, give them time to practice before moving on to the smaller **Blepharisma** and very quick **vinegar eels**. They might benefit from spending more time observing *Volvox* in the learning center.

Looking at Living Things: *Blepharisma*

Overview

Students continue in their pursuit of moving microbes. Today they hunt down the rosy colored ***Blepharisma***.

Objectives

- Students continue practicing their microscope skills on living organisms.

- Students recognize individual microbes on their slide.

- Students observe an organism reproducing by the process of binary fission.

Background

Commonly found in ponds, ***Blepharisma*** is a single-celled, pear-shaped creature about 160 micrometers in length. It is unique in its rosy coloration and therefore easy to identify.

Figure 13-1

Blepharisma *under the microscope*

Blepharisma's size varies with its nutrition. Ordinarily, its diet consists mainly of bacteria, but if its diet is enriched with other microbes, giant forms of *Blepharisma* may result. These hungry giants will then become cannibals and eat their own kind. Students probably will not witness this drama, but they certainly will notice a great variation in size among the individuals on their slide.

This microbe belongs to a group called **ciliates**. A ciliate's body is covered with short, moveable, hairlike extensions called **cilia**. These cilia act like paddles to move the microbe through the water or to set up currents to force food into its mouthlike opening.

Figure 13-2

Enlarged drawing of Blepharisma

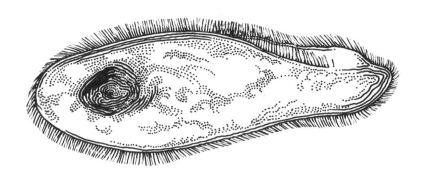

One way that the *Blepharisma* reproduces is by dividing itself in half. This process is called binary fission, and it produces two equal twins. There is a good chance that students will see one of these cells in the process of binary fission.

Figure 13-3

Blepharisma *undergoing binary fission*

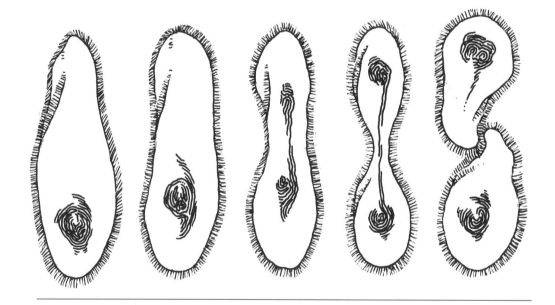

Materials

For each student

1   student notebook
1   microscope
1   very clean well slide
1   piece of lens paper
1   coverslip

For the class

    Blepharisma culture and clean dropper
1   container of clear rinse water for cleaning slides

Preparation

Set up a distribution station where students will pick up their specimen of *Blepharisma*.

As in the previous lesson, if you allow students to pick up their own specimens—and this is advisable—it will take time for them to do it carefully. Plan to provide a concurrent activity so that students are not wasting time waiting in line.

Procedure

1. Allow time for students to read the background information on *Blepharisma* on pg. 45 of the Student Activity Book. (This information is identical to the **Background** provided on pg. 77 of the Teacher's Guide.)

2. Hold a brief discussion on *Blepharisma*. Ask:

   ■ What do you expect to see under the microscope today? How will *Blepharisma* look? How will it move? How will it be different from *Volvox*?

   ■ What happens in binary fission?

3. Review the technique for mounting a living microbe in a well slide. It might even be appropriate to model it again:

   ■ Using a clean dropper provided at the station, carefully draw up a very small amount of water. *Blepharisma* tend to cluster around the kernels of wheat at the bottom of the jar in order to feed on the bacteria found there, so aim the dropper in that direction. Try not to agitate the jar or stir up the water.

   ■ Place one drop of water into the clean well slide, and put on the coverslip to prevent evaporation.

   ■ Gently return any water left in the dropper to the supply jar. Drop it in from close to the surface of the water, not from high up. It may contain many other live *Blepharisma*; you don't want to harm them.

4. During the observation period, you will want to circulate around the room, encouraging and assisting where necessary. Here are some tips for helping students get the most out of this activity:

   ■ Rather than track the *Blepharisma*, students might have more success keeping the slide in one place and concentrating on focusing up and down as individuals swim into view.

   ■ Urge students to be on the lookout for any cells undergoing binary fission. If someone does observe a cell splitting, let the rest of the class take turns observing that slide, too. You may want to set it up in the learning center for part of the day.

   ■ Ask students to try adjusting the light for different effects.

5. Remind students to include at least one drawing of *Blepharisma* in their notebook today. They might try labeling the parts. They also should write a few sentences describing what they observed, including observations of color, movement, and differences in sizes.

6. Clean up. Return specimens to the original container using the dropper again. Rinse off the slides in clean water.

Final Activities

In a brief discussion, ask students to report on what they observed. To help them focus on details, you might ask:

■ Could you estimate how many different individuals were on your slide? How could you tell them apart? (Relative size, brightness of color, differences in shape.)

■ How would you describe the motion of this microbe? (Swimming, darting, sometimes rotating.)

■ If you observed binary fission, please describe it.

Extensions

1. Interested students may want to find out more about **ciliates** (any microbe whose body is covered by short, hairlike cilia). An interesting example is the ***Paramecium***.

Figure 13-4

Paramecium

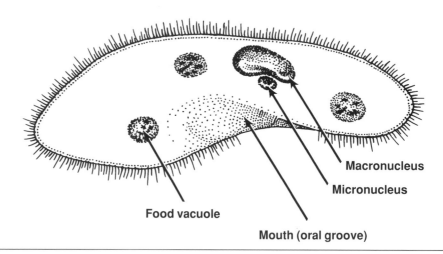

Macronucleus

Micronucleus

Food vacuole

Mouth (oral groove)

2. You may want to ask students to write a story about an imaginary creature who splits itself in half to produce an identical twin. Why did it split? How long did it take? What were their names? Did they like each other?

Looking at Living Things: Vinegar Eels

LESSON 14

Overview

In some ways, both *Volvox* and *Blepharisma* have helped to prepare students to view the **vinegar eel** successfully. Both move in unpredictable directions, both swim in and out of focus, and both display individual characteristics. Neither, however, has the vinegar eel's speed, size, or strength. Students will attempt to manipulate living specimens on a slide for the first time by trying to discover ways to contain the vinegar eel and reduce its speed.

Objectives

- Students use their microscope skills to observe a very fast-moving organism.
- Students experiment with methods for slowing down the vinegar eel.

Background

The **vinegar eel** is not a fish but, rather, a harmless roundworm about 1.5 to 2 mm long, with points at both ends. Its smooth, slender body is nearly transparent, so it is possible to see its internal organs. Made up of many cells, this creature is large enough to be seen easily with the naked eye in bright light as it moves continuously in its vinegar environment. Few would call vinegar eels beautiful, but they certainly are fascinating.

Figure 14-1

Vinegar eels under the microscope

The vinegar eel has several distinctive features. It is one of the lowest animals to have a digestive tract, complete with mouth and anus. Its method of reproduction is also distinctive. The embryos of the baby vinegar eels develop inside the female's body and are born alive and wiggling. The developing embryos are lined up inside the female's body by age, so you can see all stages of development through the mother's nearly transparent skin, if you have a powerful microscope. Another interesting feature is that the vinegar eel actually spends its entire life in **unpasteurized vinegar**—a very acid environment.

Figure 14-2

Vinegar eel with embryos

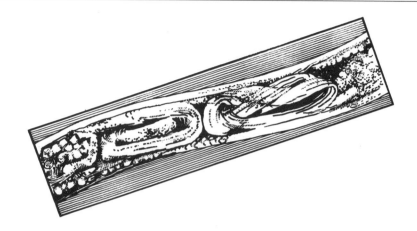

Why haven't you ever noticed vinegar eels shimmering at the edge of your vinegar bottle or swimming in your salad dressing? They simply aren't there, that's why. They live in **unpasteurized** cider vinegar, feeding on bacteria and tiny pieces of apple. But we use **pasteurized** vinegar. Pasteurization is a process of heating to a high temperature to destroy microbes. It produces **sterilized** vinegar, which completely eliminates the possibility of our finding these creatures on our kitchen shelf.

Even though the vinegar eels are quite large compared to *Volvox* and *Blepharisma*, they are a challenge to see through the microscope because of their tireless, rapid movement. They have muscles the whole length of their body and move through vinegar with powerful, whiplike motions.

Materials

For each student

1   student notebook
1   microscope
1   very clean flat slide
1   piece of lens paper
1   coverslip (or a second flat slide to act as coverslip)

For the class

Vinegar eel culture and droppers
1   container of clear rinse water for cleaning slides
Cotton balls
Tissue paper or paper towels
Unflavored gelatin

Preparation

1.   Set up the distribution station for students to pick up their own specimens.

2.   Since each student will be preparing several different slides today, you may want to provide extra slide-cleaning stations.

Students no doubt have benefited from the experience of picking up their own live specimens. This still is a slow process, however, and you would be wise to continue to provide a concurrent activity so that students who are waiting their turn at the distribution station are not just wasting time.

Procedure

1. Allow time for students to read the background information on vinegar eels on pg. 49 of the Student Activity Book. (It is identical to the information in the **Background** section on pg. 81 of the Teacher's Guide.)

2. Hold a brief discussion on vinegar eels. Ask:

    ■   What do you expect to see when you look at vinegar eels under the microscope today? How will the eels move? How will they compare in size with *Volvox* and *Blepharisma*?

    ■   How do vinegar eels reproduce?

    ■   Why don't you see vinegar eels in ordinary kitchen vinegar?

3. Demonstrate the technique for preparing a slide of a live specimen using a flat slide and a coverslip (or a second flat slide as a coverslip). This is the preferable setup because it gives the vinegar eels less space in which to move.

    ■   Using a clean dropper provided at the distribution station, draw up a very small amount of vinegar. Vinegar eels will be visible around the edge of the jar at the surface, so use the dropper in that area.

    ■   Place one drop of vinegar in the center of your clean slide, then lower the coverslip slowly into place. Try not to trap any air bubbles.

    ■   Gently return any vinegar left in the dropper to the supply jar. Drop it in from close to the surface of the liquid, not from high up. It probably contains other live vinegar eels; you don't want to harm them.

4. During the observation period, you may want to circulate around the class to encourage and assist where necessary. Here are some tips for helping students see the vinegar eels best:

    ■   As with the *Blepharisma*, students may have very little success in trying to follow the speeding vinegar eels around the slide. Instead, they would probably do better to keep the slide in one place and concentrate on focusing up and down as individuals swim into view.

    ■   If students have trouble finding vinegar eels on the slide, suggest that they try looking around the edges of the coverslip.

    ■   Remind students to try different lighting effects. Given the transparency of vinegar eels, the amount of light you use does make a difference in what you see.

5. There are a number of ways to slow down the quick little vinegar eels. Once students have gotten a look at them and appreciate how fast they can move when unobstructed, you could allow them to experiment with one or more of the methods detailed below. It is probably best not to combine the different methods; therefore, students will need to prepare a fresh slide for each one. They should clean off their slides between preparations.

- Touch a tissue paper or paper towel to the edge of the coverslip and draw off some of the vinegar. By reducing the size of the "pond," you restrict the vinegar eels to a smaller area.

- Then remove the coverslip and place several strands of cotton fiber pulled from a cotton ball on the drop of vinegar. Replace the coverslip. The vinegar eels will become trapped in the fibers.

- Try the same thing using strands of tissue paper or paper towel.

- Place a few grains of undissolved, unflavored gelatin on the slide. As the gelatin absorbs liquid and expands, it slows the vinegar eels considerably.

- If you choose to use a commercial product that slows down microscopic creatures, you should tell students to be careful to follow the directions given on the product.

6. Remind students to include at least one drawing of the vinegar eel in their notebook today, as well as a few sentences describing what they saw. The description should include mention of how the eel moves, its relative size, its color, and how the student felt observing it.

7. Clean up. Discard any specimens contaminated with fibers, gelatin, or commercial slowing products. Return any other specimens to the supply jar with the dropper. Rinse off the slides in clean water.

Final Activities

In a brief discussion, ask students to report on what they saw. Here are a few suggested questions:

- Describe the vinegar eels. How do they look? How do they move? How do they compare in size with other creatures you have seen?

- Which of the strategies for slowing them down did you try? What worked best for you?

- How did you feel observing the vinegar eels? Why was it an important activity? (Most students will say that they didn't especially enjoy looking at the vinegar eel, largely for esthetic reasons. But when pressed they will admit that it was a challenge, and they learned more about ways to control creatures on a slide.)

Extensions

1. Vinegar eels are not really eels at all but roundworms, one of the most plentiful of all animals on Earth. Roundworms can live in a wide variety of environments—soil, water, vinegar, or even inside human and animal bodies. Most are harmless, but there are some really interesting disease-causing roundworms, too. Students might be interested in doing some library research on some of the disease-causing roundworms, such as hookworms, pinworms, and trichina.

2. Here is another opportunity for students to plan and carry out an experiment. Vinegar eels live in an acid environment. Ask students to think of an experiment to find out how acid the environment needs to be for a vinegar eel to do well. Suppose you diluted the vinegar with water, for instance. How many drops of water would it take to make a difference to the vinegar eel? How could you tell it was affecting the vinegar eel? What could you observe? What could you measure? How long would it take to notice any differences?

If possible, let individual students or the class carry out the experiment.

Looking at Living Things:
Hay and Grass Infusions I

Overview

Several weeks ago, at the end of Lesson 10, the class prepared hay and grass infusions and set them aside. Now is the time to see what has developed on the microscopic level.

These next two lessons may be the most challenging of all for students; they must use all of their newly acquired expertise. This first lesson may be used for exploration, during which students discover for themselves what the infusions have produced. In the next lesson they can record and communicate their observations more completely and compare them with those of their classmates. The teacher begins to evaluate their progress in this lesson, and continues into the next.

Objectives

■ Students discover that microbes have developed in the hay and grass infusions.

■ Students begin to record their discoveries.

■ Students work independently and display a degree of ease and skill in working with the materials.

■ The teacher begins to evaluate student progress.

Background

There is no way to predict exactly which microbes may have developed in your grass- and hay-infusion jars. And, in some ways, it really doesn't matter, as long as something has. Much more important is the opportunity for students to use their newly acquired microscope skills independently in what may prove to be a very challenging situation.

It is important for students not to become overly concerned with identifying and classifying the microbes, assigning to each its proper scientific name. This is an excellent extension activity, but it is not the main focus of the lesson. Instead, students should be using microscopes efficiently and working towards distinguishing one microbe from another through their own observations. Then they will try to record and communicate their discoveries. Communicating will be further developed in the next lesson.

In order to accomplish all of this, students will need to rely on their past experience with the tools of microscopy and on their accumulated observational skills. The **Evaluation** section of this lesson (pg. 88) provides concrete suggestions for evaluating student progress in both of these areas. You may begin evaluations in this lesson and continue them through the next.

Microbes in the Hay and Grass Infusions

Things have changed in the infusion jars. If all has gone well, the hay and grass have begun to **decompose**, the water has changed to an amber brown color, a film of scum floats on the surface, and there is a definite odor when you lift the lid.

What's happening? During the first few days, **bacteria** were responsible for the changes. Most bacteria are one-celled microbes, too small to see with our classroom microscopes. They were probably on the grass, on the jar, or on your hands when you set up the infusions. Some bacteria are harmful to humans and cause disease. Others are useful and are responsible for **decomposition**, the decay of organic material (such as the hay and grass in your infusions). Think of what a mess the world would be if nothing ever decomposed!

Soon after the bacteria began to grow and multiply, slightly larger single-celled organisms appeared and began to feed on the bacteria. These larger organisms probably were also on the blades of grass or hay but in a dried-out, resting state. When conditions became favorable—when they reached water—they broke out of the protective coverings that had prevented them from drying out. Then these microbes began to feed on the bacteria and grow and multiply, too. Since there are thousands of different kinds of microscopic creatures, it is not possible to predict which ones landed in your particular infusions. So be prepared for anything. For the teacher's background information, some possible organisms are illustrated in Figure 15-1.

Figure 15-1

Some microbes you might see

Materials

For each student

1	microscope
1	well slide
1	flat slide
2	coverslips
1	piece of lens paper
1	student notebook

For the class

Hay and grass infusions and droppers

1 container of clear rinse water for cleaning slides

Cotton balls

Unflavored gelatin

Tissue paper or paper towels

Commercial slowing product (optional)

Preparation

1. Set up the distribution station for students to pick up their own supplies independently.

2. Since each student probably will be preparing several different slides today, you may want to provide extra slide-cleaning stations.

Procedure

1. Allow students sufficient time to read the background information on hay and grass infusions on pg. 55 in the Student Activity Book. This is the same information as is provided in the **Background** section on pg. 85 of the Teacher's Guide.

2. Hold a brief discussion to set the tone for today's investigations. Try to bring out these points:

   ■ No one in class knows yet what kinds of microbes we will find in the hay and grass infusions. But we are fairly certain there are microbes in the infusions. What changes have we noticed in the jars that might be evidence of their presence? (Decay, odors, changes in color.)

   ■ This is a challenging activity. The microbes will be very small and might also be fast moving. Perseverance is essential. If you don't find something on the first slide, try and try again. What tactics could you use to view these elusive creatures? (Review techniques for scanning slides and tracking creatures. Review methods for slowing down fast-moving microbes.)

   ■ How will we be able to tell one microbe from the other? (By differences in motion, color, shape, size.)

3. Explain to students what they are expected to accomplish in this lesson:

   ■ Prepare at least two good slides, one from each of two different types of infusions. Use any and all techniques learned in the unit.

   ■ Find and observe at least one microbe, and more if possible. Keep track of which infusion it (they) came from.

   ■ Make a sketch of at least one microbe, and more if possible. Label the sketches with the date and tell which infusions they came from.

   ■ Write a few brief sentences describing the microbes. Include information on their size, shape, color, and motion.

   ■ Give the microbes creative but descriptive names, which will help you remember them. For example, *Blepharisma* might be called "Pinky Pearshape."

4. Explain, too, that these are preliminary discoveries. Students will have a chance to work with the infusions again in the next lesson. You might mention that you will be taking notes on their progress in both of these lessons. While students are working, you will want to circulate around

the class to observe and begin to evaluate progress. See **Evaluations** below for detailed suggestions on the evaluation.

5.   Clean up. Have students return uncontaminated specimens to their **original** infusions. Slides also need to be thoroughly cleaned and laid out to air-dry.

Safety Reminder

Students should avoid putting hands near eyes or mouths when handling infusions. Have students wash their hands to remove any bacteria.

Final Activities

1.   Congratulate students on their progress.

2.   Ask students to share their hay- and grass-infusion discoveries with the class. They can show their drawings or reproduce them on the chalkboard and give their verbal description as well as share the name of their creatures. It will be interesting to see if other students recognize their own discoveries and whether they add to or dispute points of the description.

Extensions

1.   The question of **spontaneous generation** is an intriguing one. At one time people believed that mice sprang to life out of piles of old rags, for example. Louis Pasteur disproved the theory in a famous experiment. Interested students might want to find out what experiment Pasteur performed to disprove the theory of spontaneous generation.

2.   Provide reference books in the learning center so that interested students can identify their microorganisms by name, if they are so inclined. See the **Bibliography** for suggested references.

Evaluation

Throughout this lesson and the next, you will have opportunities to evaluate student progress in areas that touch on the major goals of the unit. The following is a description of those areas. An end-of-unit checklist is provided in **Appendix B**.

Students should demonstrate progress in these areas:

- Focusing and adjusting light easily, and tracking moving objects on the slide.

- Using good judgment in selecting the right kind of slide for the specimen at hand.

- Preparing good, clear slides.

- Working carefully, using a variety of techniques well.

- Treating living specimens with respect.

- Persistence.

- Making clear, accurate, and complete drawings.

- Using clear, vivid, accurate, and descriptive words to communicate observations.

Looking at Living Things:
Hay and Grass Infusions II

Overview

In this final lesson, students observe the hay and grass infusions for the second time. In looking again, they are urged to look more closely, to observe in more detail. They also are expected to record and communicate their observations with greater clarity and accuracy. Evaluation of student progress can continue here. Because student interest in working with the microscope may still be high, you may want to suggest one or more of the additional projects listed in the **Extensions**.

Objectives

- Students observe in greater detail the microbes in the hay and grass infusions.

- Students make more complete and detailed records of their observations.

- Students display ease and skill in working with the materials.

- The teacher evaluates student progress.

Background

After their initial explorations into hay and grass infusions, students should be ready for today's tasks. It is possible that they may see some of the same microbes again. It is also possible that these have grown, died, been eaten, or otherwise become unrecognizable. Once again, students will find themselves in a challenging situation, but they should have adequate skills and tools to meet the challenge.

Materials

For each student
  1 microscope
  1 well slide
  1 flat slide
  2 coverslips
  1 piece of lens paper
  1 student notebook

For the class

           Hay and grass infusions and droppers
1   container of clear rinse water for cleaning slides
           Cotton balls
           Unflavored gelatin
           Tissue paper or paper towels
           Commercial slowing product (optional)

Preparation

1.   Set up the distribution station for students to pick up their own supplies independently.

2.   Since each student probably will be preparing several different slides today, you may want to provide extra slide-cleaning stations.

3.   If you plan to display the products from this activity, prepare space on a bulletin board or string a rope across the room to pin them up clothesline style.

4.   Read through the **Extensions** at the end of the lesson and decide if you want the class to do any of them.

Procedure

1.   Because today's lesson is a continuation of the last one, a review seems appropriate. Try to bring out these points:

- Ask students to describe briefly the slide-making and viewing techniques they tried and which worked well for them.

- Ask students to talk briefly about what they have already seen in their infusion samples. Mention that they may, or may not, find these same creatures today.

2.   Now establish the expectations for this lesson. Stress that Lesson 15 was a warm-up—a preliminary look—but that this lesson requires more detail. Some of their tasks will be identical to what they did the last time. Some will be similar but will demand more precision. Here is what students should do today:

- Prepare one really good slide. It should be clear, without bubbles, and have visible microbes on it. (It may take students more than one try to prepare a slide that fits this description. Encourage them to keep working at it until each has made the best slide they can.)

- Find and observe one microbe in detail. If necessary, use any of the techniques you have learned to slow it down.

- Make a drawing or several drawings of different views of the microbe you observed. Label the drawing(s) with the date and tell which infusion it came from. Try to make your drawing(s) clear, accurate, and complete.

- Write a paragraph or more to describe your microbe. Include information on:

    — Size (If needed, remind students that a good way to talk about size is to compare this microbe to something else, like another microbe, a hair-width, or spaces in the screen wire.)

    — Shape, especially if it changes

- Color

- Motion

- Speed

■ Give the microbe a creative but descriptive name.

3. Explain that you will be taking notes on student progress as they work. See the **Evaluation** section in Lesson 15 and **Appendix B** for detailed suggestions of what to look for as you observe.

4. Ask students to clean up as they finish. Have them clean and return all equipment to the original containers.

Safety Reminder

Students should avoid putting hands near eyes or mouths when handling infusions. Have them wash their hands to remove any bacteria.

Final Activities

Ask students to share their final products with the class. Display their drawings and descriptions on the bulletin board or clothesline, and allow the class time to view each other's work.

Discuss ways to expand the unit if interest is still high. See **Extensions** below for ideas.

Extensions

1. Students may be interested in continuing their work with the microscope. If possible, leave a microscope, slides, droppers, coverslips, and any leftover specimens in the learning center for them to observe during unscheduled time.

2. Plan a culminating event. It might include one or more of the following activities:

■ A Microbial Lunch featuring food items made from microscopic creatures (like algae) or produced by microbes (like yogurt).

■ A Microworlds Mural featuring some of your favorite microbes.

■ Three-dimensional models of microbes.

■ An interview with a famous microbe, like the one that caused the bubonic plague, *Yersinia pestis.*

■ Individual presentations of interesting microbes, researched by students. Illustrations could be shared on the overhead projector.

Figure 16-1

Microbial lunch

Figure 16-2

Microbial mural

Post-Unit Assessments

Overview

- **Assessment 1** is a follow-up to the student brainstorming session held in Lesson 1 about lenses, magnification, and microscopes.

- **Assessment 2** is a rating scale that students can use to evaluate themselves.

- **Assessment 3** consists of suggestions for evaluating student products.

Objectives

- Students evaluate their own progress.

- The teacher evaluates student progress.

Materials

Since materials will vary, they are listed separately at the beginning of each evaluation.

ASSESSMENT 1

A Follow-up to the Student Brainstorming Session Held in Lesson 1.

During the brainstorming session in Lesson 1, students developed two lists: "What We Know About Magnifiers" and "What We Would Like to Find Out about Magnifiers." When they revisit these two lists during the assessment, students will appreciate what they have learned through their study of *Microworlds*.

Materials

The two student lists saved from Lesson 1.

Procedure

1. Display the two lists and analyze them with the students. Here are some points you might discuss:

   - Ask students to identify statements on the lists that they now know to be true without a doubt. What evidence can they offer to back up their statements?

■ Ask students to identify statements that need correction or improvement. What corrections or improvements do they want to make? Why?

2. Congratulate students on their progress.

ASSESSMENT 2 — Student Self-Evaluation

Students use a rating scale to measure their own progress.

Materials

For each student

1 Self-Evaluation Rating Scale (see pg. 95)

Procedure

1. Distribute a copy of the Self-Evaluation Rating Scale Assessment to each student and preview it with the class. Explain that it is important to stop from time to time and think about how you are working. Point out that this is a rating scale, and that only the two extremes are given. Many times students will find themselves somewhere in between. They may want to personalize the scale by adding their own descriptors.

2. Allow students sufficient time to complete the rating scale, either in class or as a homework assignment.

ASSESSMENT 3 — Evaluating Student Products

If you have kept portfolios of student products, you will find them invaluable for tracking student progress over the course of the unit. Notebooks of sketches and written descriptions, completed activity sheets, and any additional student research or reporting provide you with concrete examples of progress.

Rating Scale Assessment

NAME: _____

DATE: _____

How well did you work? Use this scale to rate yourself.

Using the Microscope (focusing, making slides, etc.)
beginner   expert

Record Keeping (drawing and writing)
nonexistent   exhaustive

Presentations
second-rate   superior

Overall Use of Time
wasted time   worked hard

Overall Feelings about the *Microworlds* Projects
negative   positive

Things I liked or did well _____

_____

Things I did not like _____

_____

Things I think I could improve on _____

_____

Next time I would like to _____

_____

Teacher's Record Chart of Student Progress

Teacher's Record Chart of Student Progress for *Microworlds*

	Student																	
Products	Lesson 1: Activity Sheet 1, Observing a Penny																	
	Lesson 2: Activity Sheet 2, Communicating Your Observations																	
	Lesson 3: Activity Sheet 3, Learning about Lenses																	
	Lesson 4: Activity Sheet 4, What Have You Learned about Lenses?																	
	Lesson 6: Two observations of black-and-white newsprint seen through screen wire																	
	Lesson 7: Activity Sheet 5, Field of View																	
	Lesson 8: Drawings of a. a hair or a feather b. a poppy seed or a sponge c. a fish scale (optional)																	
	Lesson 9: Identifications of the four unknowns																	
	Lesson 10: Drawings and written observations of assorted objects brought in by the class																	
	Lesson 11: Activity Sheet 6, What's Inside an Onion?																	
	Lesson 12: Drawings and written observations of *Volvox*																	
	Lesson 13: Drawings and written observations of *Blepharisma*																	
	Lesson 14: Drawings and written observations of vinegar eels																	
	Lesson 15: Preliminary drawings and written observations of at least one microbe discovered in the hay or grass infusion																	
	Lesson 16: A more detailed drawing of at least one microbe discovered in the hay or grass infusion and a written paragraph describing it																	
Specific Skills	Can observe closely																	
	Has learned that in order to magnify, a lens must be transparent and curved																	
	Can use a hand lens																	
	Can use a microscope: can focus and adjust light with ease																	
	Understands the field-of-view concept																	
	Can measure the relative sizes of microscopic objects either in hair-widths, millimeters, or an invented measure																	
	Can select appropriate slide (flat slide, coverslip, tape, well slide) to use with different specimens																	
	Can prepare clear, clean slides using a variety of techniques																	
	Can use the microscope effectively to view inanimate objects																	
	Can use the microscope effectively to view living creatures: can track moving microbes																	
	Has learned techniques for slowing the motion of microscopic creatures																	
	Can distinguish between a number of living microbes, including *Volvox*, *Blepharisma*, vinegar eels, and those found in the hay and grass infusions																	
General Skills	Follows directions																	
	Records observations with drawings or words																	
	Works cooperatively																	
	Contributes to discussions																	

A Supplementary Drawing Lesson

Overview

By learning to analyze the shapes of objects, students become better prepared to make accurate drawings of what they see.

Objectives

- Students learn to analyze shapes of objects as they make observations.

- Students become more aware of the elements of shape and to use these elements to draw what they observe.

Background

This art lesson stresses learning to see as a way to build confidence and lessen any student apprehension of drawing. It also should help children recognize details and translate what they see under the magnifiers into clear, simple drawings.

This lesson is adapted from techniques described in the book, *Drawing with Children*, by Mona Brookes, published by Jeremy P. Tarcher, Inc., 1986.

Materials

For each student
> Unlined paper
> Drawing materials

For each team
> A selection of varied objects with strong geometric qualities, such as:
>> sea shells
>> pecans, walnuts, or peanuts
>> seed husks
>> feathers
>> flowers

Preparation

Assemble an interesting group of objects to serve as the subjects of this lesson. Avoid rock and twigs, whose geometry is too irregular. Also avoid manufactured objects, such as bolts and nails.

Procedure

1. Tell students that they are about to learn some skills that will help them improve their drawing and make them more accurate recorders of what they see. Explain that just as you write words by recognizing and combining letters of the alphabet, you can draw pictures by recognizing and combining the basic elements of shape.

2. Hold a brief discussion of the elements of shape. According to Mona Brookes' theory, these are:

   - The dot family—anything that is rounded and colored in.

   - The circle family—anything that is rounded and not filled in.

   - The straight-line family—anything that is a straight line only, on any plane.

   - The curved-lined family.

   - The angled-line family.

3. Illustrate each shape on the chalkboard as you go along. Ask students to find examples of that shape in the room. For example:

   - for dots and circles, students might note the period at the end of a sentence, a doorknob, a globe, the moon, a cup, or a button.

   - for straight lines, students might note a telephone pole, the sidewalk, the classroom door, the chalkboard.

   - for curved lines, a paper clip, the belly of a goldfish, the end of a nose, the arch of an eyebrow.

   - for angled lines, any two straight lines that come together, like the corner of the room.

4. Now that students know what shapes to look for, distribute a set of interesting objects to each team. Briefly discuss some of the elements of shape as they apply to the objects. See the black line masters on pgs. 101 and 102. They could help.

5. Allow students ample time to observe, analyze, and then draw their objects. As you circulate around the room, talk with students about which elements of shape they see and how the elements of shape are combined in that object.

Final Activities

Ask for volunteers to display their work and analyze it in terms of the elements of shape and how they combined in that drawing.

Extensions

Obtain a print of a still life. Ask the class to describe it in terms of shapes.

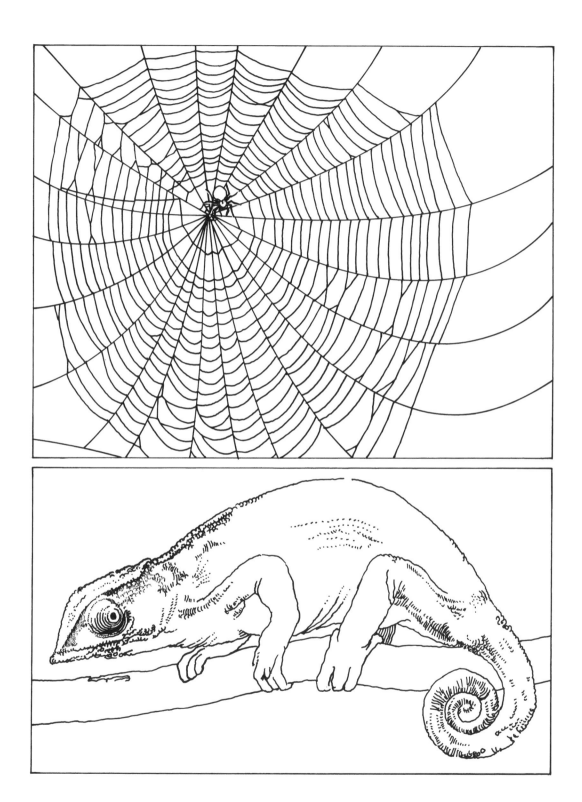

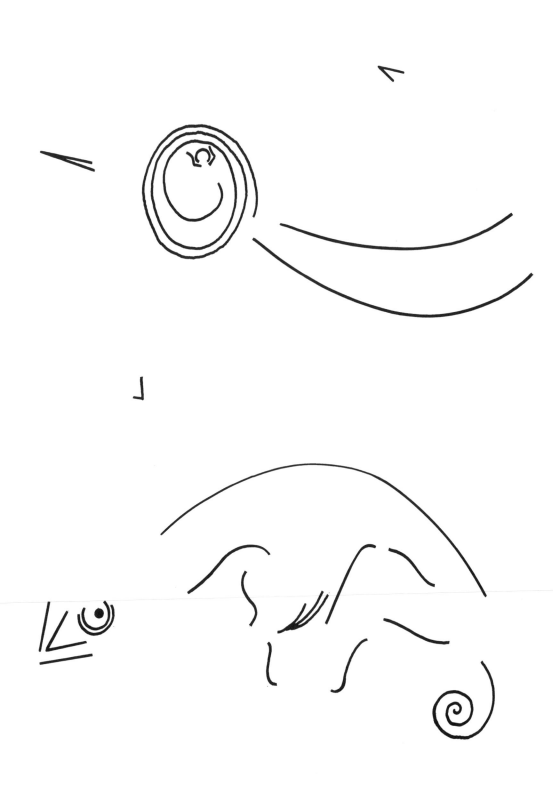

Bulletin Board/
Learning Center Materials

Each drawing listed below and provided in the following pages is derived from Robert Hooke's *Micrographia* (1665) and is reproduced here with the permission of the Special Collections Branch, Smithsonian Institution Libraries. The magnifications Hooke used for these drawings are not known. Also included in this section are full-page versions of Figure 5-1, early explorers, and Figure 10-2, Robert Hooke's compound microscope. (Note that the specimens he observed were mounted on the head of a pin and, instead of a mirrow, he worked with a shiny, curved metal reflector illuminated by a small flame.)

1. Poppy seeds

2. One kind of sponge

3. A fly and its wing

4. The head of a fly ("All the Face of a Fly is nothing almost but eyes," Hooke commented)

5. Cork

6. Silk cloth

7. A period (at the end of a sentence)

8. A bee's stinger

9. Crystals in flintstone

10. Part of a down feather

11. Fish scales

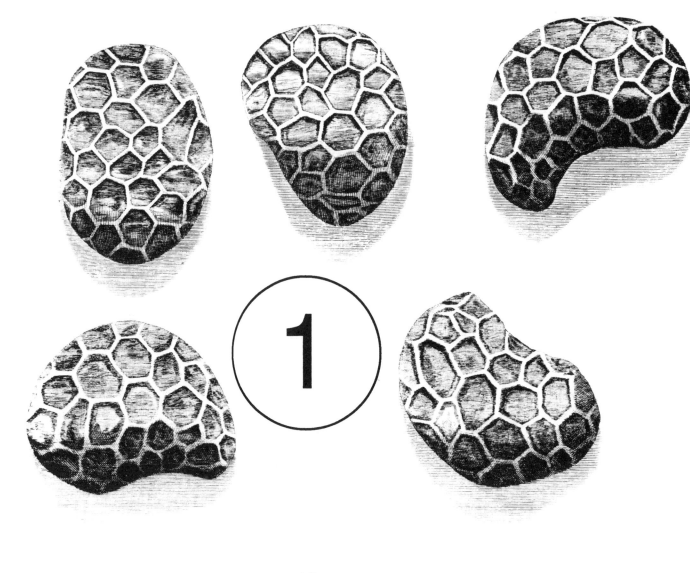

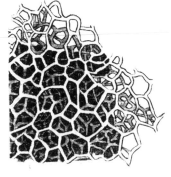

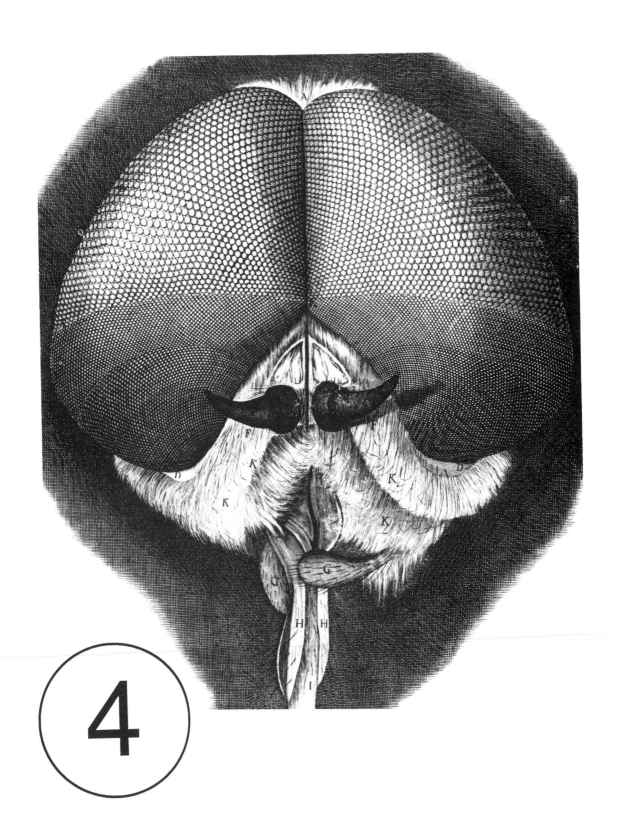

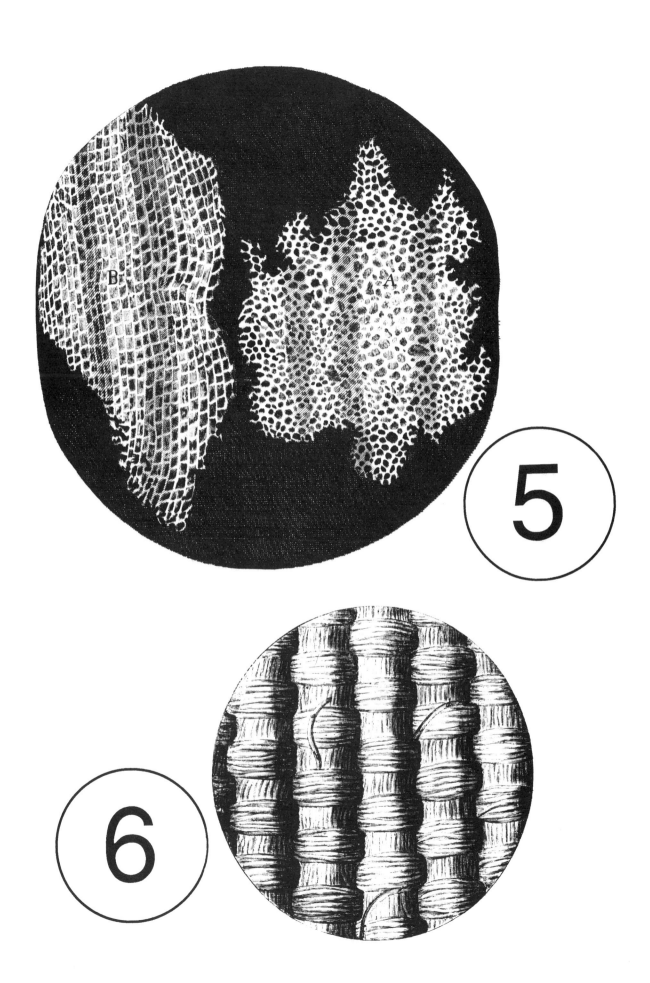

⊙A

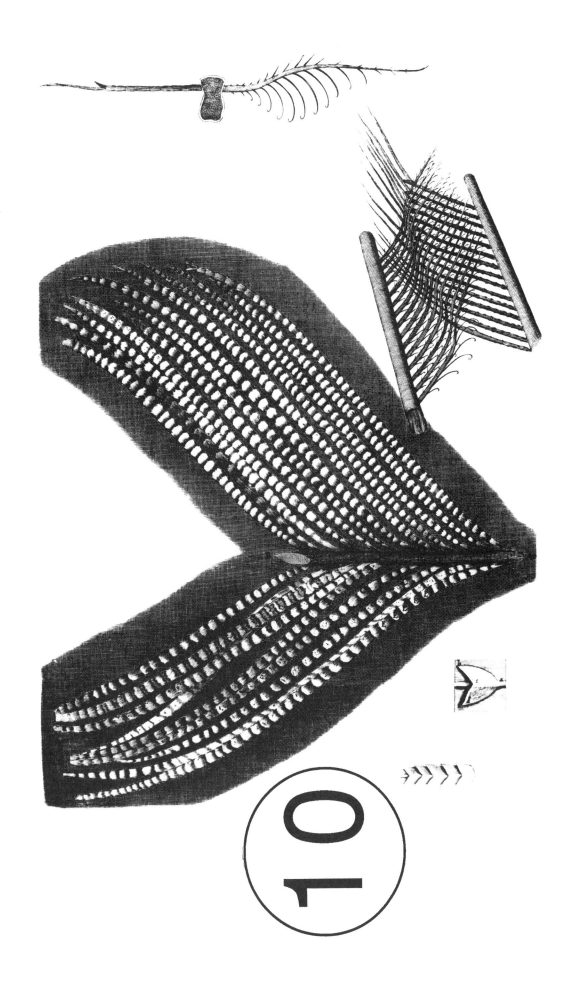

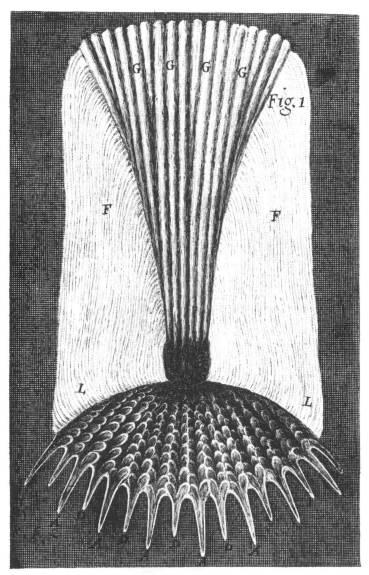

Fig.1

11

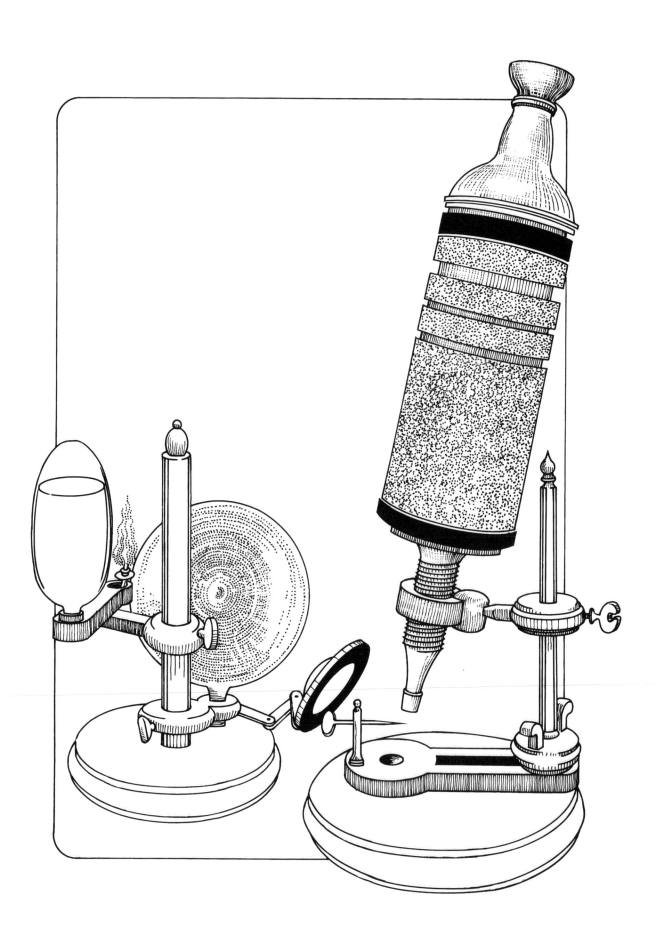

The Care and Feeding of Live Cultures

The microscopic creatures you will look at in this unit share many of the same basic needs as other living creatures: appropriate food, temperature, and light, and oxygen. Suppliers usually try to ship these to you as quickly as possible. However, sometimes due to circumstances beyond the supplier's control, the cultures are traumatized during shipment. Therefore, it is very important to see to their needs immediately upon their arrival. With the proper care, you should be able to maintain the cultures for several weeks.

For **all cultures**, do these things immediately:

- Open your shipment and remove the lids from all containers to allow in fresh oxygen.

- Place the containers in a location that allows them to adjust to the room temperature. Avoid direct sunlight and never refrigerate.

Volvox

To manufacture its own food, *Volvox* needs bright light, but not direct sun. (It would get too hot in direct sun.) A well-lighted window sill where the temperature does not fluctuate too much is fine. You also may use grow lights or fluorescent lights, which provide good illumination without too much heat.

Due to evaporation, it may be necessary to add more water. Use spring water or distilled water. Avoid tap water because the chlorine in it is harmful to many microbes. Keep the lid placed lightly over the jar to allow air circulation.

Blepharisma

Blepharisma prefers a cool (in the 70s) location. Light should be dim to moderate. An ample food supply will have been provided for the journey to you, but if you are going to keep *Blepharisma* for any length of time, it is best to set up a "wheat medium." Simply boil three or four grains of wheat for a few minutes, cool them, then place them in the culture jar. If necessary, add spring water. Keep the lid placed lightly over the jar to permit air circulation.

Vinegar Eels

Vinegar eels are very easy to keep and will multiply quite readily. They can tolerate a wide range of temperatures, and do quite well at room temperature, out of direct sun. On their journey to you, they were provided with an ample food supply that should last them several weeks. If you want to set up an additional culture of vinegar eels, it is very simple:

- Fill a small jar three-quarters full of apple cider vinegar.
- Add a small piece of apple to the vinegar.
- With a medicine dropper, transfer some of the vinegar eels to the new culture.

Debris will settle to the bottom of the jar, but do not try to clean it out. Add more apple and more cider vinegar as they are used up. Keep the lid placed lightly over the jar to permit air circulation.

Bibliography

Resources for Teachers

Arnold, Guy. *Datelines of World History*. New York: Warwick Press, 1983.

> A time line listing worldwide political, cultural, social, technological, and scientific events. A resource for integrating science and history.

Brookes, Mona. *Drawing with Children*. Los Angeles: Jeremy P. Tarcher, Inc., 1986.

> A resource for integrating art and science lessons in the classroom. This book helps you see how everything you want to draw is made up of five basic elements of shape. Specific exercises are described.

Dishon, Dee, and O'Leary, Pat Wilson. *A Guidebook for Cooperative Learning: Techniques for Creating More Effective Schools*. Holmes Beach, Florida: Learning Publications, Inc., 1984.

> A practical guide for teachers who are embarking on the implementation of cooperative learning techniques in the classroom.

Edwards, Betty. *Drawing on the Right Side of the Brain*. Los Angeles: Jeremy P. Tarcher, Inc., 1989.

> A drawing instruction book designed to build confidence.

Ford, Brian J. *Single Lens*. New York: Harper & Row, 1985.

> Recent discoveries of microscope specimens prepared centuries ago help scientists take a new look at the birth of microscopy.

Grave, Eric V. *Discover the Invisible*. Englewood Cliffs, New Jersey: Prentice-Hall, Inc., 1984.

> A useful guide to the microworld. Gives a brief history of the early micronauts. Identifies many of the more common microbes. Provides clear photographs.

Headstrom, Richard. *Adventures with a Microscope*. New York: Dover Publications, Inc., 1941.

> Ideas and explanations for the truly curious. The book offers suggestions for interesting observations. This is a good teacher resource.

Headstrom, Richard. *Adventures with a Hand Lens*. New York: Dover Publications, Inc., 1962.

> Common objects are viewed from a new perspective. Simple line drawings and explanations make this an excellent teacher resource.

Hellemans, Alexander, and Bunch, Bryan. *The Timetables of Science*. New York: Simon and Schuster, 1988.

> A chronology of the most important people and events in the history of science. A resource for integrating science and history.

Johnson, David W., Johnson, Roger T., and Holubec, Edythe Johnson. *Circles of Learning*. Alexandria, Virginia: Association for Supervision and Curriculum Development, 1984.

> This excellent book presents the case for cooperative learning in a concise and readable form. It reviews the research, outlines implementation strategies, provides definition to the skills needed by students to work cooperatively, and answers many questions.

Resources for Students

Darling, David J. *The Microchip Revolution*. Minneapolis: Dillon Press, Inc., 1986.

> A brief history of the development of the computer, the invention of the microchip, and other revolutionary developments in microelectronics.

Gennaro, Joseph, and Grillone, Lisa. *Small Worlds Close Up*. New York: Crown Publishers, Inc., 1978.

> Remarkable black-and-white photographs of common objects magnified hundreds to thousands of times. A favorite for all levels. The text is brief.

Oxlade, Chris, and Stockley, Corinne. *The World of the Microscope*. London: Usborne Publishing Ltd., 1989.

> A practical introduction with clear text and ample illustrations. Provides step-by-step instructions on how to make slides. Covers different types of microscopes, and suggests many projects.

Paige, David. *A Day in the Life of a Police Detective*. Mahwah, New Jersey: Troll Associates, 1981.

> A picture essay with brief text highlights investigative techniques and the use of a forensics laboratory in solving crimes.

Selsam, Millicent E. *Greg's Microscope.* New York: Harper & Row, 1963.

> An easy reader emphasizing common things that Greg observes with his microscope. May be helpful to a child who has missed several lessons.

Simon, Seymour, *Hidden Worlds: Pictures of the Invisible.* New York: William Morrow & Company, 1983.

> An exploration of things you cannot see around you, inside you, and out in space. Microscopes, telescopes, X rays, and high-speed and infrared photography reveal the invisible world in black and white as well as in color.

Wilkin, Fred. *Microscopes and Telescopes.* Chicago: Children's Press, 1983.

> Describes the parts of a telescope and microscope in detail, and tells how to use them properly. Easy-to-read text. Color photographs.

Materials Reorder Information

During the course of hands-on science activities, some of the materials are used up. The consumable materials from each Science and Technology for Children unit can be reordered as a unit refurbishment set. In addition, a unit's components can be ordered separately.

For information on refurbishing *Microworlds* or purchasing additional components, please call Carolina Biological Supply Company at **800-334-5551**.

National Science Resources Center Advisory Board